D1228902

FROM THE ASHES

$$\text{WATTS} = \frac{\text{VOLTAGE}^2}{\text{RESISTANCE}}$$

—*Ohm's Law*
(George Simon Ohm,
1787-1854)

FROM THE ASHES

Voices of Watts

EDITED AND
WITH AN INTRODUCTION BY

BUDD SCHULBERG

THE NEW AMERICAN LIBRARY

Third Printing

Published by The New American Library, Inc.
1301 Avenue of the Americas, New York, N.Y. 10019
Published simultaneously in Canada by
General Publishing Company, Ltd.
Library of Congress Catalog Card Number: 67–27434
Printed in the United States of America

Acknowledgments

All anthologies are difficult to gather and organize, but it is easier when one is dealing with established authors and even established places of residence.

In the case of *From the Ashes,* we are publishing eighteen writers, nearly all of whom have never been published before. We were selecting those eighteen from approximately thirty contributors to the Watts Writers' Workshop. We were choosing roughly 100,000 words from more than 300,000 submitted. In many cases the writers are without telephones. The everyday "emergencies" of ghetto life also contributed to the difficulty in assembling this material.

Faced with these unusual editorial problems, I owe a special debt of gratitude to Mrs. Arabel Porter, senior editor of The New American Library, who approached this project not only with great professional skill but truly as a labor of love; to Miss Fredericka White, my editorial assistant, who functioned both imaginatively and efficiently in tracking down missing writers and their material and, herself a young writer of promise, contributing her own creative judgment; to Mr. Ted Simmons, Deputy Director of the Pacific Coast Writers' Conference at Los Angeles State College, who has been working with our Watts poets' circle — my thanks for his generous contribution of time and effort; to Mrs. Donna Cannon, a young professional writer and editor, who enthusiastically volunteered her time to both screen and type a profusion of manuscripts; to Miss Juanita Watkins, who also generously volunteered her services at Douglass House and typed many manuscripts there; to Mrs. Ad Schulberg, who waived her usual literary agent's fee and worked above and beyond the call of agenting to represent the economic interests of the group; to her similarly dedicated secretary, Miss Nancy Boylan; to Sally Bowman, who served with efficiency and deep concern as secretary to the Workshop in its early months of accomplishment and travail; and to Mattie Smith, who has given loyal assistance to Harry Dolan, chairman of our Writers' Council and manager of Douglass House.

Although they were not involved directly in the putting together of this book, others deserve mention for their contribution to the progress of the

Watts Writers' Workshop in general; from this progress emerged *From the Ashes.*

Stuart Schulberg, with outstanding style and taste, produced two national television shows, *The Angry Voices of Watts,* August 16, 1966, and *Losers Weepers* by Harry Dolan, February 19, 1967, which attracted national attention to the writers of Watts.

Irving Stone's interest in the Watts poetry first published in *Los Angeles Magazine* led to his urging his literary circle to support the Workshop, and from his associates, Professor Allan Nevins, Irving Wallace, Professor Stanley Wolpert, Mort Lewis, Justin Turner, and others came our original financial assistance. Irving Stone has continued to serve as an active member of the Advisory Board, along with James Baldwin, J. Alfred Cannon, M.D., U.C.L.A. Clinic of Neuro-Psychiatry, Judge Harry T. Shafer, Claude Brown, Dr. Fred Mayer, Mr. Stan Sanders of Watts and Yale University Law School, and The Reverend Morris Samuels.

We are also indebted to Mr. John Steinbeck, who contributed first his enthusiasm for the work that came to his attention, then his personal check, finally his recommendation to Mr. Roger Stevens that The National Foundation on the Arts and Humanities, of which Mr. Stevens is chairman and Mr. Steinbeck a council member, provide a grant to encourage and expand the literary activities of Douglass House. In his letter accompanying the grant approval, Mr. Stevens has expressed his keen and sympathetic interest in the Watts Workshop as a "pilot project" that may open the way to similar efforts in other ghettos. He and the other officers of The National Foundation — Charles C. Mark and Carolyn Kizer — happily oriented toward art rather than bureaucracy, have in a very real way also played their part in the making of this book.

Finally, indispensable to this project is the devotion of my wife, Geraldine Brooks, who pored over manuscripts with me through many days and nights and offered both profound companionship and wise counsel in the difficult and delicate job of creating the final table of contents.

— *Budd Schulberg*

Contents

Introduction

It was Black Friday, the 13th of August, 1965. Like millions of other dazed or complacent Los Angelinos, I was watching an unscheduled "spectacular," the damndest television show ever put on the tube. Not long before, I had written an introduction for a new edition of *The Day of the Locust,* in which Nathanael West projects a Hollywood art director whose masterwork is an apocalyptic canvas entitled "The Burning of Los Angeles." West's painter saw his vapid, vicious city consuming itself in angry flames. Here, on television, in prime time, in fact around the clock for eight days that shook not only Los Angeles but the entire country, was Nathanael West's nightmare vision as if it had leaped from the canvas and was coming *live* from Watts.

Not only Watts but all of south-east and central Los Angeles was being put to the torch. Television cameras hanging from helicopters brought the action into our living rooms. Flames from the supermarkets were licking into the sky. Crowds were looting pawnshops, drugstores, liquor stores, radio-TV stores, clothing stores, and all the other establishments that had been quietly looting the community on the installment plan over the years.

An effervescent Negro disc jockey, Magnificent Montague, had popularized the phrase "Burn, Baby, Burn!" for a platter that sizzled on his turntable. Now his innocent zest became a battle cry — not burn with musical fire but with real, live, crackling, dangerous, revolutionary fire. To the frightened Caucasians living in their white ghettos far to the north and west of the barricades, "Burn, Baby, Burn!" was an ominous and threatening invocation. But to the black people who finally had taken possession of their own streets, "B3" — expressed in the symbol of three fingers raised jubilantly into the humid summer air — was charged with revolutionary zeal. It was the "Don't Tread on Me" and "Damn the Torpedoes — Full Speed Ahead" of the Rebellion of Watts.

We at home were watching nothing less than the on-the-scene telecast of civil war. For make no mistake about it. This was no riot. A riot it may have been in its first, spontaneous hours. But as the hated Los Angeles Police Department now tried to contain what they had triggered, it transformed itself into a genuine, full-scale Revolt, a rebellion that had been years in the making in the festering black ghettos of Los Angeles, a rebellion the affluent city of the white man was unaware of because he was looking *north* and *west* while hundreds of thousands were sweating out poverty, hunger, unemployment, the lack of education, transportation, recreation, and hurting with the humiliation of it all, to the *south* and *east*.

Abruptly, the "dramatic" pablum spoonfed to us happy vidiots by our patronizing sponsors was flung from our trays. Into our living rooms raged an element that is usually forbidden on television — *life,* and its dark, red underbelly, *death.* Not spurious, TV-gunsmoke death but the undignified red hole in the flesh and the unrehearsed crumple of the wasted corpse — the real thing. A ragged army of thousands was surging through the burning streets spewing their hatred of white cops and "white devils" in general. The angry black braves found excitement and release in the fires lighting up the skies over the city they considered their Enemy.

A guest in my house for this impromptu television show was a New York columnist who had come to write funnies on Reaganland, and the hippies of Sunset Strip, and topless waitresses serving luncheon pizzas to pie-eyed patrons of the arts. Los Angeles is a "pigeon" at point-blank range for visiting humorists. But this time our guest had a serious question:

"What the hell is going on down there?"

I didn't know. The more I watched the more I realized that I had no idea what was going on down there. Or if I knew the *what,* I could make only an educated guess at the *why.* But I knew it only in my head. And it wasn't something one could read up on in books. I had read my share, from the autobiography of Frederick Douglass, to Dr. Clark's *Dark Ghetto,* the angry essays of Baldwin, and the abrasive *Autobiography of Malcolm X.*

What was I to do? As an American writer, still oriented toward social fiction, I felt an itch, an irresistible urge to know. I held to the old-fashioned notion that an author has a special obligation to his society, an obligation to understand it and to serve as its conscience. Melville and Whitman had known this. So had Twain and Howells, Norris and London, Sandburg and MacLeish, Sinclair and Dos Passos, Wright and Steinbeck. The responsible American writer makes it his duty to report on his corner of the nation. Los Angeles is my corner. I was raised here. I had gone to Watts in my youth to hear T-Bone Walker and other local jazzmen in the honky-tonks of what was then a small rural chunk of the South tossed into the outskirts of the crazyquilt sprawl that was and is Los Angeles. In the Sixties, Watts was no longer six thousand but sixty thousand; the black ghettoland of South Los Angeles had leaped to 600,000 in an exploding county population of six million. Still the bottom-dog tenth.

I was there in Los Angeles. I was self-appointed to go to Watts while the fires were still smoldering. If I were to understand this urban tragedy, it would require not merely a look but a lot of looks, and not merely superficial looks but finally, somehow, from the inside looking out.

So out of lush, plush, white, bright Beverly Hills, my New York columnist friend and I drove south to the Santa Monica Freeway and east to the Harbor Freeway, and turned off on Century Boulevard, which runs from the twenty-first-century silhouette of the International Airport on the west to the dilapidated railroad station of Watts on the east. The first cliché reaction of the traveler to Watts is: why, what's all the complaining about? This looks a hundred percent better than Harlem — or the Negro slums of any Eastern city. Look at the nice, wide, tree-lined streets and the attractive little individual houses with their neatly trimmed flowerbeds and their well-kept lawns. Yes, there are such houses, block after block, and the first impression might be of a comfortable lower-middle-class city in the Midwest. We found sunshine in Watts, and a deceptive suburbia, with small palm trees. But when we took a harder look we could see that the palm trees were growing like the people, as if they really did not have their hearts in it. Moving on beyond Success Street, we came to 103rd Street, the mainstream of Watts, which had won notoriety as Charcoal Alley No. 1. I had not seen such devastation since, as a member of an OSS team in World War II, I had driven into German cities to collect incriminatory documents. Burned-out supermarkets were smoldering. Pawnshops and liquor stores were piles of rubble and shattered glass. There hung over Watts that terrible silence that descends on battlegrounds the day after battle.

Just off embittered 103rd Street we saw a pale-green two-story stucco building. It stood alone now because everything around it had been burned to the ground. This was the Westminster Neighborhood Association, a social service agency backed by the Presbyterian Church. There were a few shabby offices and some bare classrooms and a recreation room that looked more like a forlorn pool hall. Troubled young men were being encouraged to come in off the hot streets where there was nothing to do but grumble about the Man and how he finally had thrown more firepower at the brothers than they could handle. Westminster was offering classes for illiterates, teen-age and adult. There was a dancing class, lacking instruments or a record player, and some basic English and Negro-history classes. In an unadorned assembly hall kids banged on an old out-of-tune piano and formed spontaneous singing groups and put on haphazard variety shows. There was some psychiatric help and efforts to assist severely depressed families in the nearby housing project, and that was about it — a sad, far cry from the great settlement houses teeming with self-improvement in the old East Side Jewish ghetto of New York.

An energetic, plain-talking young social worker from Harlem and from CCNY guided this first tour of Miseryland, the dark side of the shimmering Angeles moon. In the poolroom I tried to shake hands with young men whose eyes would roam the floor and the walls when mine sought to meet theirs. No, they would not put out their hands in that somewhat meaningless gesture of greeting our white civilization cultivates.

"Most of these brothers have just gotten out of jail," our spirited escort from CCNY explained. "Some of them were leaders in the Revolt. Others were just standing on corners watching when they were handcuffed and dragged in. Even before the Revolt it was a miracle if a young man on the streets without a job could avoid building up a record. Once they've got a record it's practically impossible to get a job. Not that there are jobs to get — in rich, beautiful L. A. we've got an unemployment problem worse than the country had in the Depression thirty years ago."

One of the teen-agers, very shabby and very black, missed his shot at the lumpy pool table and growled at me, "I was on a motherfuckin' chain gang in the South. Every goddam day the man takes me out and beats my ass. Finally I get away and hitchhike to L. A. New Scene. Another chance. Two days later I'm busted here. Not doin' nothin', jus' huntin' me a place to sleep. The man picks me up and whops on me jus' like back home. Shi-it, man, I had it with whitey." He glared at me and turned back to his game of pool.

"I didn't mean to get you insulted," said our guide. "But if you come down here you might as well see it like it is. I don't have to tell you these kids are hostile. They feel so trapped and kicked around. We don't want to turn off their hostility and turn them into Uncle Toms. We want to guide them so they can turn those energies into constructive channels. It's discouraging. Every day there's a hundred human crises. I figure if we help one in a hundred we're doing something."

I sat down on a box behind a group of young teen-agers who were staring dully at daytime television on a set from the middle Fifties. I squirmed when the commercials came on. Like most litterateurs I am conditioned against commercials. The cigarette sells and the instant relief from body odors — it's all too much and we laugh at it, put reverse-American on it, and accept it as part of the game. It's camp to comment on how much more you enjoy the commercials than the so-called entertainment sandwiched in between, and to have your easy chuckle at the expense of Marlboro and Rear Guard and Mr. Clean. But I said *squirmed.* My first afternoon in Watts I knew I had never looked at TV that way before. It was eerie to watch these man-children watching the promised land held up to them through the magic of the television tube: look but don't touch. They were dropouts and they were jobless and some of them slept in doorways and in the backs of cars, prey to police harassment and the vices that seem to offer momentary escape. And what was the commercial offering them? — an opportunity to get in on the ground floor of a new real-estate developer's dream, each individual split-level home facing the golf course, and of course each with its own swimming pool, "no longer a millionaire's prerogative but within reach of even the budget-minded homemaker."

"Shi-iit, man! I think I'll buy me two of 'em, one f' my white maid." They broke themselves up. They were laughing, but it wasn't good-natured, easy laughter. It was their own, stylish way of reacting to a challenge, a brutal challenge of a society that was selling swimming pools and golf courses and at the same time warning them to keep off the grass.

I remember feeling, after watching them watch that absurb American Dream of a commercial, that the burning of a supermarket (offering substandard meats and vegetables at higher prices than in Beverly Hills) was, if not forgivable, at least understandable.

From the pool hall we walked over to the Jordan Downs Housing Project. The units are adequate for young married couples who can afford eighty-five dollars per month. But God or Allah help you if you have four, five, or six children — or more frequently eight, nine, and ten. Walking back to the beat-up Westminster building, the crude beginnings of what may one day become a thriving settlement house, I heard myself asking the inevitable question of the concerned white visitor: "Is there anything I can do? Is there anything one person — not an organization, but just a single person — can do?"

"Just because our kids are mostly high school dropouts doesn't mean they're dumb. I can show you dropouts with IQ's of a hundred and forty. These kids are so frustrated they're going out of their minds. Some of them literally. They need motivation — stimulation. You said you were a writer — maybe you could start a writers' class."

These days I receive letters from ghetto neighborhood groups in Cin-

cinatti and San Francisco and Philadelphia asking how I began, as if there were some special magic we bottled to launch our Watts Writers' Workshop. I simply posted a notice on the Westminster bulletin board — "Creative Writing Class — All interested sign below." Simple as that. It would be pleasant to add that a dozen aspiring young writers signed immediately and we were off and writing. The truth was, nobody signed up. Nobody came. Week after week I sat there like an idiot shepherd without a flock, shuffling my notes and idly reading the community papers in the small, cluttered room that was actually a kind of pantry for the Westminster kitchen. Sometimes I wandered down Beach Street to 103rd. People glared at me. I felt unwanted. I could catch the tone of angry muttering. "Dig the gray beast! What the fug you think he's up to?" Sometimes I'd be confronted directly. "The white man's heaven is the black man's hell!" a lean, ragged youngster who looked and sounded like a teen-age Malcolm would challenge me as I passed.

What to do? Give up? Admit that a white man, no matter how altruistic he believes his motives to be, has no place in a black ghetto? I decided to tough it out. At least to try it not for three weeks but for three months if necessary — or longer. But I thought I would try new tactics. Nobody knew me on Beach Street. Nobody could figure out what I was up to. It was still only a month or so after the curfew had been lifted and the National Guard withdrawn. One Hundred and Third Street was still suffering from a sense of psychological siege. White was fuzz. White was power structure. White was "Travelin' Sam Yorty" the Mayor and his Police Chief Parker, against whom the people of Watts seemed to feel a hatred similar to the feeling of the Jews for Hitler and Himmler. White was the color of the Enemy that held you in and blocked you off and put you down and kept you there at the business end of the billyclub and the bayonet point.

I thought I would try, as a calling card, the film *On the Waterfront* that I had written. Since the street kids who were my prospective students had no money to go to the movies, I suggested to some staff members at Westminster that I might talk to the manager of a local theater — get him to run the picture for us at some off-theatrical hour that would not compete with commercial showings. My suggestion trailed off. I could see the Westminster workers looking at each other.

"Don't you know there's no such thing as a movie theater in Watts?" one staff member said.

"You've got to go all the way up to midtown, a good ten or twelve miles, about two dollars round trip," said the other.

So I borrowed a sound projector and a 16 millimeter print of *Waterfront* and we ran the picture in the makeshift Westminster assembly hall. It was mid-September, 1965. It was like a midsummer night, suffocatingly hot. There was no air conditioning. Not even fans. Our audience consisted of thirty restless teen-agers, some of them from Westminster's Youth Training and Employment Program, some of them hard-core trouble kids, troubled and trouble-making, some of them on glue and dropping red-devils, thrill-seeking some escape from the demoralizing atmosphere of a neglected community.

All of a sudden there was a commotion across the street. A crowd was forming in front of the prosperous two-story building cater-cornered to our center. "This place is in a worse depression than the country as a whole was in the early thirties," said an angry staff worker. "But that shop over there does the best business in town." He was referring to the mortuary.

I looked around and realized that I had lost my audience. I followed them to the street and learned the nature of the competition. A six-month-old baby had died. The mother's grief was intensified by the bitter knowledge that the prompt arrival of an ambulance and a hospital closer than the County General Hospital a dozen miles away might have saved her child.

So, outside the mortuary on Beach Street while my movie was running in an empty room, I was learning another important lesson about Watts. Nearly all the things that we take for granted uptown as part of the comforts of city living are brutally missing in Watts. In an area of large families and inadequate housing, prone to accident and the illnesses of undernourishment, there are fewer doctors and substandard medical care. The laying-out of that infant during the "premiere" of *On the Waterfront* in Watts still burns in my mind as image and symbol of the true meaning of medical deprivation.

You may read in the $300,000 McCone Report that "the Commission believes that immediate and favorable consideration should be given to a new, comprehensively-equipped hospital in the area." The authors of this report go on to describe an urgently critical situation in the comfortable language of bureaucratic polysyllables. They fail to look into the face of the bitter young mother who sees her infant sacrificed to "statistics indicating that health conditions of the residents of South Central Los Angeles are relatively poor and facilities to provide medical care are insufficient." "Relatively poor, hell!" cries Watts. "What health conditions? Insufficient medical care — those are just a lot of big words for the murder of our children!" Yes, and then they add, dangerously, "If they were your babies dying, you'd have an ambulance there in five minutes and a good hospital close enough to save them." Invariably, someone in the crowd would call out, "Brother, tell it like it is!"

In Watts I have heard it said over and over again, "You know what the real trouble is — nobody cares. You white people uptown don't give a damn about us. Hell, even our middle-class Negroes who move out to Compton or west of the Freeway don't care about us. That's why we don't have a hospital and we don't have hot meals and we don't have a movie house and we don't have a bus system that'll take us to the job interviews, and we don't have — "

One tries to say that there are thousands in the comfortable white neighborhoods who are not complacent about segregation and poverty-stricken ghettos. But one of the tragedies is that there has been no real channel of communication between Watts and the prosperous communities, between Watts and what you might call "The outside world." Watts has been made to feel cut-off, neglected, ignored, rejected: an explosive social condition.

In those early months — despite the pontifications of Field Marshall McLuhan — I refused to lose faith in the word. I continued to hope that we would find some communication through the word, through words put together meaningfully to communicate frustrations, feelings, thoughts, ideas.

At last my first recruit arrived. Although he is not represented in this anthology, I shall always be grateful to him. Some of his spirit, some of his determination to rise from the ashes, breathes in this book. Charles Johnson. Nineteen years old but looking a dozen years older. Round-faced, pudgy, but, you felt, not a man you'd like to mess with. A veteran of the County Jail during the Revolt. A veteran of a lot of things. I had met him on that first visit to the pool hall. He had told me how the police had busted him while he was standing on a corner watching the fires. "I don't have to tell you what they did to me — I can show you the marks," he had said quietly.

On that first visit Charles Johnson talked with me for almost three hours. Just the two of us. Starting very slowly. Feeling each other out. Groping. Searching. After the first hour it got easier. I think both of us were a little surprised that we could talk to each other as honestly as we did. He asked me what my purpose was in setting up this class. "Nothing up my sleeve," I said. "It's just that I'm sick of people talking about the problem — The Negro Problem, as the whites call it, The White Problem as *Ebony* calls it — and not doing something personal about it. I'm not the anti-poverty program. I'm not the N Double-A CP. I'm just me, a writer, here to see if I can find other writers."

"Now I'll tell you the truth," Charles said. "Some of the brothers didn't like the sight of you. In fact some of them wanted to stomp you. But I told 'em, 'Lemme see what the cat is up to first!' "

Thus Charles Johnson became the charter member of the Watts Writers' Workshop. "I got things to write about," he said, "only I don't know if they're stories." He told me a few. I said, "Stories aren't fancy things. They're the things you've been doing, what you did in the uprising last month, what you're thinking about now."

Our first textbook was *Manchild in the Promised Land* by Claude Brown. Charles Johnson and I read some of it out loud together. By the time he was nine years old Claude Brown was a manchild, a respected thief and full-fledged member of the Forty Thieves. At thirteen, when the white kids of suburbanland are playing Little League baseball and going on cookouts with their dads, Claude was lying on the dirty floor of a fish-and-chips house in Harlem with a bullet in his gut.

Putting the book down after a particularly vivid excerpt, Charles Johnson said, "Wow! That's a real tough book. I didn't know you could put words like that in a book. Sounds just like we talk on a Hundred and Third Street. Everything he puts in that book, that's just like what's going on here in Watts. I could tell a hundred stories just like it."

Sometimes Charles would bring a friend with him, a gangly, homeless teen-ager who is considered retarded. Call him Luke. I had been warned that Luke could become violent and that unaccountably he had attacked a Westminster staff worker. Sometimes Luke would wander into the empty little classroom and sit down beside me and, with his dark, sad, sensitive face only a few inches from mine, stare at me while Charles and I were discussing a possible story. It was unnerving, but somehow Luke and I got used to each other. He did not write, although Charles said he had interesting ideas. He sketched surprisingly well.

And this derelict, whom some considered a village idiot, was strangely dependable. Later, when our original cubbyhole was preempted and we were shunted to some other makeshift classroom, a sign would have to be posted telling prospective members where to find us. Luke would take off on his long, cranelike legs and the notice was posted impeccably and punctually. Luke was not writing, but he seemed proud of the writing class. He seemed pleased to have these little jobs to do. In order to understand Watts and the creative element so alive in Watts, it may be necessary to understand Luke. When the police pulled him out of the back of a parked car — his bedroom of expediency — and locked him into the hated 77th Street Precinct on the usual charge of suspected armed robbery, a crowd of many hundreds marched on the jailhouse. They were trying to tell the police something about Luke. They were trying to say that Luke needs more than an overcharge of robbery and a hard time in jail. The police did not get the message. They spoke to the protestors with shotgun butts.

By this time the writing class was growing. There was a mysterious eighteen-year-old who had dropped out of Jordan High School in his junior year, the same year he had left the home of his stepmother and ten half-brothers and sisters, living thereafter from hand to mouth with many meals not passing from hand to mouth for many days. He looked like a shy, unathletic, unkempt, underdeveloped Cassius (What's-My-Name?) Ali. He handed me a poem, on a small scrap of paper, in longhand. It was titled, "Infinite." By Leumas Sirrah. I paused after the first line: "Never know a begin of me." "Begin?" I thought, You can't use *begin* as a noun. But something whispered to me, "Wait a minute, before you jump to grammatical improvement, say the line again." *Never know a begin of me.* It may be one of those original lines that goes on beating in your head long after the impeccably Victorian lines have died like cut flowers. Every week after that Leumas Sirrah would hand me three or four new poems, "Godandman," "You and I," "Who's Life," "One, Two, Three" — and say: "Criticism." But like "Infinite," these poems were both complex and original and deserved more than instant criticism. I would have to take them home and ponder. With Leumas came another teen-age high-school dropout, Ernest Archie Mayhand, Jr., who shared with Leumas the chancy, marginal life of the child in search of his manhood, his identity in the dark ghetto. He listened, and indulged in long, philosophical discussions with Sirrah regarding the latter's abstract, metaphysical poetry questing for God, unity, and identity.

Our young poet's corner on Beach Street was joined by older prose writers who found their way to us by word of mouth: roly-poly, half-defeated Harry Dolan, in his middle thirties, in the process of being retrained as a glass-blower to support his four children, arrived with a battered briefcase full of unfinished manuscripts. He had been everything from a porter at Filene's in Boston to a city-hall janitor to a weekly Negro-newspaper reporter. Time was running out for Harry Dolan. But he still wanted to prove that he should be a writer and not a glass-blower or a janitor. Since this was a workshop, my job wasn't to teach Harry

Dolan how to write or even what to write — the real stuff of ghetto life beat strongly in all the scraps and false starts and incomplete rewrites he had to show. The job was simply for Harry Dolan to organize himself, his material, his talent. He seemed to have everything but self-confidence. Pick the piece you like best, concentrate on it, don't stop until you know it is the best you can do with it, get a clean, finished copy, and move to the next: that was about all the teaching I had to offer Harry Dolan, and from this gentle nudge flowed essays like *Will There Be Another Riot in Watts?,* short stories like "I Remember Papa," plays like *Losers Weepers.*

There was also Birdell Chew, a lady in her fifties, like so many Watts residents a migrant from the rural South, a philosophical veteran of the hard life, active in the struggle of the community to pull itself up from the depths of despair and neglect and apathy and a tragic sense of alienation from the white overlords.

Like Harry Dolan, Birdell Chew had been wanting to write all her life. My first reaction to the first chapter of her novel in progress — years in progress — was similar to my impulsive response to Leumas Sirrah's first line of "Infinite": "Looks hopeless — can't spell or punctuate — trips over her own syntax — semi-literate." But I took it home and made only the most necessary, simple, grammatical adjustments. Our secretary — by now we needed a special secretary for the workshop writing alone — typed a clean copy. When I read the first chapter of Birdell's book again, it was like looking through a window that had been cleaned after gathering dust and crust for years. Suddenly everything was clear, and beautiful in its simplicity. The two little swamp children caked with mud and ignorance who make their profound discovery at the far end of their glades say something about the meaning and impact of education in a fresh and original way. Birdell Chew took literally our Workshop maxim: "Write only what you know." A lady had dropped off a fetching, shy six-year-old child at Birdell's modest house in Watts, asking Birdell and her daughter to baby-sit for the day. The mother never returned. Birdell loved this "adopted" daughter and decided to write a story about her. In her first version it was a three-page sketch of a story. Class by class the story evolved until it became a full-length story, "Lady Linder." At one Workshop session we read all four versions — from its brief, tentative beginning to its final copy — to study how a story grows. Regretfully, its length prevents its inclusion in this collection.

Other would-be and should-be writers came, people who had been working at it all their lives and were yet to be published, like James Thomas Jackson, from Temple, Texas, who had drifted into Watts from

Houston, by odd coincidence, on the first night of the uprising. His greeting from Los Angeles was to be stopped by police without having the faintest idea of what was going on. James Jackson has been trying to hold himself together by sweeping out the hoary Eagle Cafe on South Western Avenue. His class references are sprinkled with quotations from Melville and Hawthorne, and once when he mentioned Fitzgerald he added: "I'm talking of Scott now, not Edward, though I dig a lot of Edward Fitzgerald too." Mr. Jackson has written a dozen chapters of a novel about a Negro army unit in World War II — *Shade of Darkness.* I only had to read a few chapters to know we had another genuine writer in our group.

And then there was Sonora McKeller, born and raised in Watts, known all over the area as "Aunt Fanny," a militant community action worker recognized for her cleanly written and strongly delivered speeches to anti-poverty groups. Sonora is also a human melting pot, part Afro-American, part German, part Apache Indian, part Mexican. She has been everything from a chorus girl to a South Los Angeles Joan of Arc.

There was twenty-year-old Johnie Scott, who drank wine and dropped red-devils with the most abandoned of the desperate black children of 103rd Street, but who survived, miraculously, to become one of the handful of his generation in Watts to graduate from Jordan High School and to find his own eloquent voice as a kind of poet laureate of ghetto Watts.

And Jimmie Sherman, high school dropout, who had also gone through a period of personal rebellion, turning to wine, marijuana, and gang-fighting, but who was now a reformed ex-GI teaching boxing at a Teen Post, who filled out his application for the Workshop with the significant phrase: "I had made up verses since I was a little boy, but it was taking part in the Revolt of Watts and thinking about what it had meant to me for days afterwards that made me realize that what I really wanted to be was a writer, not just for myself but for all of us who want justice in America."

By the spring of '66 we had outgrown the small offices and classrooms we had been using at Westminster. Westminster itself was bursting at the seams as its various anti-poverty, self-development programs multiplied. So we moved up to 103rd Street, on good old Charcoal Alley No. 1, into the Watts Happening Coffee House, an abandoned furniture store that the young people of the area have transformed — industriously and ingeniously — into an art center. There are home-made paintings on the wall, a few of them fascinating, a lot of them promising, some of them god-awful. There is a stage where poetry readings and self-propelled plays like Jimmie Sherman's *Ballad from Watts* and musical entertainments are performed weekly. There are happenings and political discussions that lean toward extreme Black Nationalism, and a record player that swings everything from the Supremes and Lou Rawls to grand opera.

The Watts Writers' Workshop was adding new members at every meeting. Young poets Alvin Saxon, Jr. ("Ojenke"), and tall, willowy, vague and deep Emmery Evans. A forty-year-old from Indianola, Mississippi, who had been the first Negro to graduate from Brigham Young University, Harley Mims. Our first Mexican contributor, warm, enthusiastic Guadalupe de Saavedra. Young, black, militant, and talented Vallejo Ryan Kennedy. A twenty-year-old product of 103rd Street who stammers badly but whose words pour out on paper with a "deep blue feeling," Edna Gipson. Young matrons in their early thirties, Jeanne Taylor and Blossom Powe, of the *Ebony*-reading middle-class, who seemed to find fresh inspiration in brushing shoulders with the troubled or angry kids of the Watts ghetto.

By summer '66 our Writers' Workshop was becoming a kind of group-celebrity. *Los Angeles Magazine* published the poetry of Johnie Scott, Jimmie Sherman, and Leumas Sirrah, and they found themselves attracting national attention. *Time* Magazine reprinted some of the poems with an article in the Education section on new approaches to school dropouts in the ghetto. NBC-TV devoted an hour on prime time to "The Angry Voices of Watts" — Johnie Scott, Harry Dolan, Leumas Sirrah, James Thomas Jackson, Birdell Chew, and Sonora McKeller reading their poems, essays, and stories under the imaginative direction of Stuart Schulberg, whose camera roamed the main streets and back alleys of Watts as the writers became their own narrators.

A moving poem like Johnie Scott's "Watts, 1966," could be brought to life realistically on brooding, blistering 103rd Street. But the abstract, metaphysical poetry of Leumas Sirrah was a puzzling challenge. "How would you illustrate your poem 'Infinite'?" Stuart asked Leumas. Leumas, high school dropout, on probation, police-harassed, penniless, living the desperately marginal life of the manchild in the unpromised land of Watts, went off to meditate. In a few moments he returned. His answer was a question: "Are you able to photograph a teardrop?"

Stuart promised to try. For weeks he and his integrated camera-crew guided by our workshop writers photographed and recorded what had been considered dangerously unphotographable — the angers, fears, frustrations, and teardrops of the inner ghetto. The program was presented on the first anniversary of the holocaust and the national reaction was like Charles Johnson's "Wow!" The reviews from coast to coast read like love letters. NBC monitors reported that there were more phone calls and letters for this program than for any since the Huntley-Brinkley telecast of the Goldwater Election Night debacle.

I do not mean to suggest that everything was hunky and dory. There was many a hard day's night in the Coffee House. The Man was still a target for abuse and I was the only one available. Young angries would walk up to our large circle and heckle: "Absurd! A white man trying to teach black men! What can a white cat tell the brothers about art? We've got soul, man! You ain't got no soul. You got white shit in your heart." Other angries would bang the piano or the bongos to drown out the poets or turn up the hi-fi until it sounded as loud as the siren of the police cars forever screaming up and down 103rd Street, the shrill and ever-present voice of the Enemy.

One day we tried a writing exercise: to choose the one word that would sum up the aspirations of Watts, with a five hundred-word explanation. Harry Dolan said, "A Chance." Birdell Chew said, "Justice." Ernest Mayhand said, "Respect." Leumas Sirrah said, "Identity." Jimmie Sherman said, "Dignity, or pride."

A young painter on the periphery of our group burst in with fierce impatience:

"Why fool around with a lot of fancy words for what we want? We all know what we want — freedom. It's the one word. Without freedom we aren't alive. We're walking dead men. We can't wait for your President's Great Society. . . . "

He was interrupted by a teen-ager who had taught himself to play moving jazz on the clarinet and flute: "What's the use of writing what we want? We've been trying to say what we want for years, but who listens to us? We're not people. If you really thought we were human beings you wouldn't allow us to live like this. Just look up and down this street. The rubble hasn't even been cleared away. It's full of rats. All of us have been raised with rats. Uptown you're sleeping two in a king-sized bed and we're sleeping four in a single bed. A game of checkers or setting up little Teen Posts won't solve this. If we were some foreign country like the Congo, you'd be worried that we might go Communist and you'd send us millions of dollars to keep us on your side, but here at home you just take us for granted. You think you've got us on the end of your string like a yo-yo. Well, we're not going to hang on that string anymore. . . .

We're ready to take our stand here and to die for our freedom in the streets of Watts."

White readers, and perhaps some Negro readers as well, do these words frighten and shake you? I heard them week after week. Many evenings I walked out of the Coffee House, into the oppressive darkness shaken and frightened by the depth and intensity of the accumulative anger.

A full year had passed since the Fires of '65. Despite the faint claims of the Honorable John McCone, there had been few objective changes in Watts. A year later there was still no hospital, still no movie theater, still no recreation center, still no transportation, still no jobs, still no day-care nursery, and still no genuine concern from the city authorities. And yet there were some unmistakable signs that Watts was not stagnating. It was undergoing some profound psychological change. A prominent local psychiatrist, Dr. Frederick J. Hacker put it this way:

> What the McCone Commission fails to understand is that from the standpoint of the lower-class Negroes living in Watts, the riots . . . were not riots at all but a revolution. They thought of themselves as freedom fighters liberating themselves with blood and fire. It could be argued that the Negro community was much better after the riots than before. Because the riots served as a safety valve against the feeling of apathy that was the strongest characteristic of life in Watts.

Camus in his profound essay on man in revolt might have been writing about Watts '65 when he said, "Resentment has been defined as an auto-intoxication — the evil secretion, in a sealed vessel, of prolonged impotence. Rebellion, on the contrary, breaks the seal and allows the whole being to come into play. It liberates stagnant waters and turns them into a raging torrent." And later, "The spirit of rebellion can exist only in a society where a theoretical equality concedes great factual inequalities."

Albert, amen. The black militancy, the feeling that it was too late for integration, that the Blood had had it with the Man, was tragic but understandable, especially in a vast conglomerate city-suburb like Los Angeles, where it was galling for the black man on the bottom to salute the flag of one city distinctly divisible, with liberty and justice for the affluent white and the complacent middle-class. But a big question remained. Having shucked apathy for militancy and subservience for a new pride in Negritude, would the post-Revolt Afro-Americans of South Los Angeles express their new attitude and personality through more fires and snipers and molotov cocktails or through creative acts of self-development and self-fulfillment?

The answer came in late summer '66, when a new spirit of unity and a fascinating ambivalence toward the white man produced "The Watts Summer Festival." The angry young blacks, some of whom found their poetic voices in our Workshop or through their paintings and indigenous jazz, were ready to take to the streets. There was talk that they would celebrate the Six Days That Shook Los Angeles a year before by moving out into restricted neighborhoods and burning whitey out. Gun stores reported a run on weapons in white communities and black. Sounder (or more creative) heads prevailed. But they were not the City Hall Uncle Toms or the middle-class Negroes who had "made it" and moved away from Watts and South Central Los Angeles, never to look back or lend a hand to their ghetto-locked brothers. There was a new breed of militant Negro leadership personified by young men of proven ability like Stan Sanders, the first Rhodes Scholar from Watts (who now serves on the Advisory Board of our Writers' Workshop), who was able to go to Oxford and later to Yale Law School. Stan and a team of young progressive nationalists decided to turn a potential violent outbreak into a peaceful demonstration of community alliance and productivity. I referred to *ambivalence* because the Watts Summer Festival was double-edged. If it resisted the temptation to invade the white man's terrain, it was also a joyous celebration of a victory, a victory for lawlessness and disorder in search of identity and freedom.

Watts — August '66 — was neither snarling nor trying to play "good dog" and sit up and do tricks for the happy and relieved white man. It was celebrating a new-found sense of power. There was dancing in the streets, dancing such as Los Angeles has not seen since its true Mexican fiesta days. And instead of fires along Charcoal Alley No. 1 there were great tents displaying jazz groups, exhibitions of sculpture, and paintings. There were street plays and street entertainers that revived the flavor of commedia dell'arte. In the Coffee House, Jimmie Sherman presented his *Ballad from Watts*. Studio Watts performed its own interpretation of Genet's *The Blacks*. And our Writers' Workshop, now grown to some twenty members, gave a nightly program of readings — a historic literary moment for Watts — the first time its writers were being heard on a stage, reading from their own works.

For three days this unique Arts Festival went on, and lo, the miracle —

in all that time, even with the bars of 103rd Street going full blast (and that's a *blast,* baby!), there was not a single incident. With white tourists all over Watts, not a single ugly or dangerous moment. Here at last was law and order. But whose law?

In a rare mood of forbearance, the provocative Los Angeles Police Department had agreed to withdraw completely from "The curfew area," the city hall euphemism for the ghetto. Instead the policing was left to the Watts Summer Festival Committee, which drew on the young black nationalists to maintain that magic balance called "law and order." I saw youthful Leroi Lam, foolishly accorded a full page in *Life* as the "dangerous nationalist Leroi Ali," cruising 103rd Street on a scooter, courteously directing civilian traffic. White visitors poured in from their comfortable pockets in the enormous pool table of Los Angeles and they were greeted not only with hospitality but with unusual efficiency.

The young men responsible were the same ones who had created — prior to the festival — a possibly unprecedented community organization, the Community Alert Patrol. Before and after the festival they used cars resembling black-and-white police cars, got hold of cameras and walkie-talkie equipment, and when arrests were being made — always a tense moment when white men are handcuffing and sometimes also cuffing black men in the ghetto — the CAP was on hand to photograph and record any use of excessive force. Their presence produced an unusual atmosphere of calm. Contrast this to the more typical kind of experience involving one of our Workshop members in the Appendix to this book.

What does an indigenous police force have to do with an Introduction that is supposed to devote itself to a literary awakening in Watts? Since there is no border guard who stands on the boundary between life and art, the indigenous self-protection and supervision of the Watts Summer Festival may be as creative as the contents of the festival itself.

When it was suggested that we find an over-all title for our Workshop readings in the Watts Happening Coffee House, Johnie Scott and some other articulate members were critical of "The Angry Voices of Watts," because they felt the title was narrow and self-limiting. "Of course we're angry but we're not *only* angry," Johnie said. And others broke in: "It seems to us we're also trying to be thoughtful —," "— or to remember our childhoods —," "— or to be self-critical." "Or maybe even just funny once in a while," Harley Mims added. So it was put to a vote, and after heated discussion there was a landslide victory for "From the Ashes." The writers of Watts were expressing the hope not only of their twenty-odd voices but of the entire community. From the ashes, out of the rubble, out of apathy, despair, neglect, and hopelessness might rise a black phoenix. "Our job is nothing less than to rebuild this ghetto from the ground up and from the inside out," Sonora McKeller said. It was in this spirit that Sonora and other writers in the Workshop read from their works during the significant Watts Festival.

But it was merely an uneasy truce. Once more the mailed fist of the L.A.P.D. came down on Watts. Watts was marked as the hard pit of the bitter ghetto fruit and there was constant harassment. Young men were picked up for loitering, for being on the streets after midnight, for having no definite address, and on suspicion for all sorts of crimes. When the troopers struck, our young writers felt the blows along with the others. The Watts Happening Coffee House was a particular target. To the unemployed, the dropouts, the angry, talented young people of 103rd Street, the Coffee House had special meaning because it wasn't a Teen Post, a government hand-out, but *theirs,* their very own — from the paintings covering the walls to the furniture they had made with their own hands. Three or four of our homeless young poets were sleeping there on the sofas. When they and their friends emerged, they were intercepted by nervous officers of the law and forced humiliatingly to spread-eagle against the wall while they were searched for arms and dope. Some of our teenagers, at times wearing yellow Malcolm X sweatshirts, would see the feared police cars and run. The white helmets would assume that flight was a confession of guilt. "I don't think they were arresting us as individuals," said Leumas Sirrah, "I think they were arresting our sweaters."

On the day the eighteen-year-old Leumas was to receive our poetry award at a presentation in the Westminster Assembly Hall, he was in jail "on suspicion of armed robbery." Some of his friends from the Workshop were with him when he was busted. They knew he had never carried a gun. We wanted Leumas out of jail to receive his award.

So we turned to our friend "Golden Boy" Art Aragon (the hottest boxing attraction in California ring history) who was now a bail bondsman with a card that carried the old Golden Boy touch: "I'll get you out if it takes ten years." Leumas was out in time to accept his prize at our first Watts Writers' Awards. He was photographed and interviewed. He shied away from publicity. There were television news cameras that he tried to avoid. "The more the police see me the more they'll arrest me," he said. I thought he was exaggerating. But the next day Leumas was arrested again for "armed robbery." It happened that this alleged crime took place exactly at the time when Leumas had been receiving his parchment at the Westminster assembly. I discussed it with Leumas' probation officer. "This isn't law enforcement, it's clearly harassment," I said. This time there were hundreds of witnesses to testify as to where Leumas was on the morning of the crime. Even the television cameras. Father Morris Samuel, a swinging white Episcopalian priest on the staff of the almost 100 percent Negro Westminster Neighborhood Association, went over to the 77th Street Precinct himself, and as in the earlier case, without Leumas ever being brought before a judge, the charges were dropped.

But the arrest record was growing. Soon it would be so long that young Leumas would be virtually unemployable or unable to complete his education, despite his dreams of doing so. "But I ought to thank the police department," says Leumas. "They have presented me with an opportunity to put my thoughts in writing." That is his wry way of describing the many days and nights he has spent in jail prior to charges being dropped.

Captain Tom King of the 77th (who later did an energetic if futile job of trying to prevent Harry Dolan's teleplay *Losers Weepers* from being produced in its natural locale in Watts) may not realize what a center for the arts he is conducting in his celebrated gaol.

In a real if inadvertent sense, Captain King and his unsmiling lieutenants and sergeants, may be credited with an assist in the founding of the Frederick Douglass Writers' House that has risen from the ashes on Beach Street, a few blocks down from Westminster in the heart of Watts. For it was after the second, or perhaps the third arrest of Leumas, after a protracted stay in the county jail for some other of our Workshop poets, during a period in which I often found myself roused in the small hours for the latest emergency, that I came to a full awareness of what I had begun. It had been naïve or callow to think that I could go to Watts for three hours of a single afternoon once a week. A creative writing class in Watts was fine, as far as it went, but it didn't go very far for writers who were homeless, who had to pawn typewriters, who fainted from hunger in class. Most of these writers would fall apart because they had no address, no base, no center, no anchor. That discovery was the genesis of Douglass House, named in honor of Frederick Douglass, the runaway slave who taught himself first to read and then to write, memorably, who became one of the most powerful speakers in the cause of abolition and who founded and edited the influential newspaper *North Star*. Frederick Douglass had fought his way up from the cruel beatings and heavy chains of professional slave-breaker, to discover the power of the word. A slave of illiteracy, of the cold-blooded *system* of illiteracy, he had become his own master and a master of the language of his land. It was Frederick Douglass who wrote:

> If there is no struggle, there is no progress.
>
> Those who profess to favor freedom, and yet depreciate agitation, are men who want crops without plowing up the ground. They want rain without thunder and lightning. They want the ocean without the awful roar of its waters.

The beginnings of Douglass House could not have been more unprepossessing. We drove up and down the streets of Watts looking for vacant houses until we found a nine-room house, literally in ruins, but with possibilities. All the windows were shattered. Glass and unspeakable debris littered every room. It could be rented for ninety-five dollars per month. I thought I could swing that personally while I worked on some primitive plan to renovate and support the house by other means. The writers themselves cleared away the litter. How, I wondered, were we to raise the money to rebuild the house, furnish it, equip it with typewriters, a reference library and the other tools of our trade, pay the salaries of a resident manager, a secretary and editorial assistant . . . ? It was both gratifying and alarming to find ourselves becoming a kind of spontaneous institution receiving frequent requests for literary contributions, for appearances on TV and radio programs and at creative and educational seminars and conferences, for press interviews with individual writers. The BBC wanted to film readings to be telecast in England. *West* Magazine commissioned a piece by James Thomas Jackson on the founding of Douglass House. Irving Stone had expressed his astonishment at the quality of the poetry of Scott, Sherman, and Sirrah. Would he contribute twenty-five dollars per month or three hundred dollars per year to support Douglass House? Yes, he would, and so would associates in his informal writers' circle, Professor Stanley Wolpert, head of the History Department at U.C.L.A., historians Mort Lewis and Justin Turner, Professor Allan Nevins, and Irving Wallace. We began to reach out to friends across the country and the world, and, almost magically it seemed, checks began to pour into our Douglass House account: from James Baldwin in Istanbul, Irwin Shaw in Klosters, Switzerland, the Richard Burtons in Rome, Steve Allen and Ira Gershwin in Hollywood, Herbert Gold in San Francisco, Senator Robert F. Kennedy and Art Buchwald in Washington, Richard Rodgers, Ann Petry, Dore Schary, Paddy Chayefsky, and Frank Loesser in New York, Harry Golden in North Carolina, Hodding Carter in Mississippi, Elia Kazan in Connecti-

cut, John Steinbeck in Sag Harbor . . . and more as the months went by.
Steinbeck's check was accompanied by an interesting letter:

> I saw the product of your project on television. I was astonished at the quality of the material. Some of it was superb. For one thing I was impressed with the growth of these people. I am so tired of one-note writing, sad homosexuality is not enough as a working tool for a writer. Your writers have learned early that one is not aware enough to scream with pain if one has not had glimpses of ecstacy. And both belong in our craft — else there would be neither.

Then John Steinbeck, ever a practical man, an old-fashioned American who can fix and make things with his hands, added a paragraph that was characteristically pragmatic. Writing individual appeals to fifty or sixty writer friends must be enormously time-consuming, he said; since he was a member of the Council for the National Foundation for the Arts, he would like to recommend to Roger Stevens, head of the National Endowment, that the Watts Writers' Workshop receive a grant from the Foundation. It seemed to Steinbeck that the literary workshop we had going in Watts was exactly the kind of project they would want to endorse.

By irony, or signs in the heavens, or crazy luck, which may all amount to the same thing, the day that we were to deliver our written appeal and budget to the foundation was the same day a delegation from our workshop was invited to testify before the Ribicoff Committee holding hearings in Washington on urban dislocation, disorientation, decomposition, and everything else that is eating away at the core of the megalopolis. Harry Dolan looked at Senator Ribicoff and said: "I tell this to you now, *you* being all of white America, so that you will not be able to say, as the Germans tried to say when they were told about the concentration camps and the gas chambers, 'We did not know!' " Johnie Scott has developed his testimony in the form of an essay included in this book, *The Coming of the Hoodlum.* Huntley-Brinkley played back part of this testimony on the evening of his appearance and *The New York Times* judged it worthy of two columns of newsprint and a follow-up editorial by Tom Wicker.

Written statements by veteran ghetto anti-poverty fighters Sonora McKeller and Birdell Chew were also entered in the *Congressional Record.* My own testimony came to this conclusion:

"If instead of the creative talents we have begun to tap in Watts — and Watts is everywhere, from South Los Angeles and San Francisco, to Hough in Cleveland, and the south sides of Chicago and Philadelphia —

if, instead of the creative talent to be discovered underground, another kind of treasure was going to waste, if *oil* was not being brought to the surface but instead was being allowed to seep through the ground and be wasted, then I can hear the business community, the practical business-minded, $olid-citizen$ of America crying, 'Wait! What a waste! We must save it! Channel it! Money is being lost!'

"Well, this is another kind of oil, another natural resource, a human resource seeping down through the earth, through the underground, the subculture. And surely it calls for an equal amount of efficiency, an equal amount of fervor, if we are not to continue to squander a part of our wealth, our spiritual wealth, our young manhood, and particularly the black young manhood that not only Scott and Dolan but a score of our writers could testify is going to tragic waste in all the ghettos of America."

When I first put up that notice, "Creative Writing Workshop," in Watts I had no idea what I might discover. But I do now. I have no illusions that our Workshop has cornered all the writing talent in Watts. New writers wander into Douglass House with their stories and poems in hand almost every day. And what of the musical talent, the painting and sculpture like Noah Purifoy's imaginative "junk" put together and recreated literally from the rubble of the Revolt? Or the natural acting talent that may be symbolized by Sonora McKeller, an amateur who more than held her own with tremendous effect in the midst of powerful professional Negro actors in Mr. Dolan's *Losers Weepers?* Deep into my second year with the Douglass House writers of Watts, I am convinced that there are Leumas Sirrahs and Harry Dolans and Johnie Scotts and James T. Jacksons and Harley Mimses and Alvin Saxons all over America, wasting away as janitors or menials or unemployed. I am reminded of Gray's *Elegy* — often the poem comes back to haunt me — and it may yet come to haunt us all if we do not heed its lesson: Thomas Gray walking through an obscure graveyard, and wondering what would have happened if these people unknown in their potters' graves had not been neglected and overlooked, what might have happened if they had been given their full share, their full chance:

> Perhaps in this neglected spot is laid
> Some heart once pregnant with celestial fire;
> Hands, that the rod of empire might have swayed,
> Or waked to ecstasy the living lyre.

And a few verses later:

Some village Hampden that with dauntless breast
The little tyrant of his fields withstood,
Some mute, inglorious Milton, here may rest,
Some Cromwell guiltless of his country's blood.

The writers of Douglass House — and the Douglass Houses waiting to be founded all over America — may or may not be Miltons. But for too long they have been mute and inglorious. My experience convinces me that the young, angry social worker who first greeted me in Watts was telling me the stone truth. There in the poolroom lurks the nuclear physicist, lost to drug addiction through criminal neglect and want of motivation. There on the street corner drifts the young poet who flunked English in the tenth grade. And finally, who is flunking, he or we? The society, the school, is flunking. The substandard ghetto school, the race-ridden society, is the biggest Dropout of them all. Think about it, Mr. and Mrs. America, as Walter Winchell used to say. And young Miss and Master America. But don't think about it too long. The time is too short and the cost too great. Think of finding these young men of mysterious depths, of talents neglected, before the poet or the lute player goes to his pauper's inglorious grave. He may be only one among a thousand, or ten thousand. But he may find, like an Ellison, a Claude Brown — perhaps now a Harry Dolan or a Johnie Scott — that he speaks for a hundred thousand, or for twenty million. His single candle may light a thousand thousand candles. And the light and warmth of these candles may help redeem and regenerate the core of the ghetto, that decomposed inner city, waiting either for a phoenix to rise from the ashes, or for bigger and more terrible fires.

The ambivalence and ferocious complexity that I have found in my two years in Watts is expressed profoundly in the wide range of attitudes and feelings within our Workshop now grown to thirty members with thirty-five new applicants as we go to press. There is a young element with deep distrust of the white man and with strong leanings toward black nationalism and separatism. There are older members, no less militant but oriented toward American justice in the form of integration. Some are swayed in both directions. There may even be a few of what old and loving but also firm and fierce Birdell Chew calls "crawling, creeping Uncle Toms." Somehow they have learned to coexist in the Writers' Workshop, containing their differences and even their opposite poles.

I have been asked if I am not afraid of the angry young men of Watts who are said to contemplate guerrilla warfare. I am more afraid of the greed and selfishness and the blind intransigence and the appalling ignorance of social dynamics that build concentration-camp walls around enclaves like Watts. Because as we have learned from the freedom fighters of Berlin, when a tyrant builds a wall the tyrannized will not rest until they have pierced it or torn it down.

There are many ways to build a wall and as many ways to level it and remove it. To make of this Introduction a round, Claude Brown and I spoke recently at a symposium at Pomona College. After the conference Claude spent his last day in Los Angeles in Douglass House in an open-end bull session with the half-dozen residents and other members of the Workshop who dropped in to meet him. "I've never seen anything like this," said Claude excitedly. "Kids who were running the streets just like I was in Harlem are spending the whole afternoon reading poetry to each other, and listening to each other. They've got a real, live creative atmosphere going here, man! That's worth more than a whole calendar-full of conferences on what to do about ghettos."

So we began with loner Charles Johnson and the retarded Luke cutting the Workshop's baby teeth on the tough street language of *Manchild.* We close with that Manchild come to Watts to share his experiences with the overlapping experiences of his brothers in Douglass House. On the second anniversary of the holocaust that began as a riot, developed into a rebellion, and then settled down to the longer, harder task of constructive revolution, Douglass House is ready to play its part in the emergence of an Afro-American renaissance that could be as significant as the artistic renaissance of Harlem in the 1920's, and hopefully longer-lived.

And now I see the curtain going up. Ladies and gentlemen, kind and not so gentle readers, on with the book. Let the burned chips fall and lie and smolder where they may. And then, optimistically, may they be gathered together and reassembled, like the memorable "junk" art of Watts that is rising *From the Ashes.*

— *Budd Schulberg*
Douglass House, Watts
1967.

HARRY DOLAN says that one purpose of his writing is to make "all the paradoxes of my life funnel to one point." There have been many paradoxes since he was born in November, 1927. For example, when he went into the Navy and became head of his unit, a subordinate told him he "wouldn't take orders from a nigger." Again, when he was stationed in an all-white town, and shortly after he was told by police that "niggers" were not wanted, he saved the police chief from a mad killer. Also, he missed the GI bill for college because "I couldn't get sixty dollars together and feed my family too." Now, as a Workshop member, and with his wife's encouragement, he was decided to make writing his career. In early 1967 his TV play, *Losers Weepers,* produced over the NBC network, won national attention. (Mr. Dolan appeared in a small role himself.) In May his story, "I Remember Papa," was sold to *Esquire,* and he continues to write: he has written a sequel to *Losers Weepers* — another play, *Love Song for a Delinquent* — and has contributed a number of short stories to the Workshop, which he joined early in 1966. He now serves as chairman of the Douglass House Writers' Council.

I Remember Papa

The other night after attending a gratifying function which had been initiated to help the black man, specifically to help build a nursery for children of working mothers, and after seeing and hearing white people make speeches professing their understanding and desire to go to any length to help, I found myself suddenly cornered and forced to defend the fabled laziness of the black man.

What was especially surprising was the fact that I assumed this white acquaintance — since he had paid thirty dollars to attend this dinner held for the purpose of helping the black man — did, at least in part, have some sympathy with what his, the white people, had tried to accomplish.

As I stood there watching his eyes I became suspect of my own sincerity, for I stood attentively nodding my head and smiling. I lit a cigarette, raised an eyebrow, performed all of the white man's laws of etiquette, and all the while I knew if it had been others of my black brothers, they would have cursed him for his smugness and invited him outside to test his theory of black man's courage and laziness. Of course I did none of these things. I grinned as he indicated in no uncertain terms that as soon as the black man got off his lazy butt and took advantage of all the blessings that had been offered him for the last two hundred years, then he, the white man, would indeed be willing to help.

I could have answered him — and was tempted to, for he was obviously sincere. Instead, I found an excuse to slip away and let a white man fight my battle, a friend, even a close friend. I went to a far corner and blindly played a game of pool by myself as the voices of this man and my friend dissected me. I stacked the pool balls, leaned over the table, and remembered a black man I had known.

It was said of him later in his life that he had let his family down. He'd been lazy, no-account, a troublemaker. Maybe so, maybe so, but I can't help remembering nights of his pacing the squeaking floor muttering to himself, coming back across the floor, sitting down, his legs trembling as he listened to the woman plead for him not to do anything bad.

"I'll go to hell first before I'll let you and the children starve." God, how many times had I heard him say that! How many other men standing bunched in helpless stagnation have I heard vow to take a gun and get some food for their children! Yes, they were planning to commit a crime; yes, they were potential criminals. Then. They are usually black too — another crime, it seems.

I remember that man, but more I remember his woman, my mother. Curiously though, I never remember her dancing, running, playing; always lying down, the smell of disinfectant strong, the deep continuous coughing, the brown paper bag filled with the toilet paper red with bubbly spit and blood, lying half concealed under the bed.

I never remember her eating food such as bread, meat, potatoes; only apples and only Delicious apples. In those days five cents apiece. She was a small woman, barely five foot.

"Junior," she would say softly. She never spoke above a whisper. "Go to the store and get me an apple." The thin trembling hand would reverse itself and slide up and under the covers and under the pillow and then return as though of its own volition, the weight almost too much, and as I'd start out the door, she would always smile and say, "Hurry, Junior."

I'd nod, and always, always there seemed to be a need to hurry. Those trips were always made with a feeling of breathless fear. I didn't know why then, only that for some reason I must always come back as soon as possible.

I was returning with an especially large apple, walking along, tempted to bite just a tiny piece, when I turned the corner and saw the black police ambulance standing in front of my door. Suddenly I had to go to the bathroom so bad I couldn't move. I stood watching as two uniformed men came out with the stretcher, and then the sound of my mother's shrill voice hit me.

"Mama, Mama," she was screaming. I could see her twisting and swinging at the lady next door as she was held back. I stood there feeling the hot piss run down my trembling legs, feeling cold chills spatter through my body, causing frozen limbs to spasmodically begin to move. I forced myself toward the police wagon as the men opened the doors and slid the stretcher along the bare metal. I saw my mother's head bounce on the floor.

"Wait," I moaned, "don't hurt her." Then I was running, screaming, "Please don't hurt her."

I looked down at her pain-filled face, and she smiled, even then she smiled. I showed her the apple. The effort to nod seemed a terrible effort but she did, her eyes so very bright, so very shiny.

"You eat it, Junior, you and sis."

"What's wrong, Mama?" I asked softly. "You really, really sick now?"

She nodded.

"Your father will be home soon. Tell him I'm at the General Hospital. Tell him to — to hurry."

"I'll tell him, Mama," I promised. "I'll tell him to hurry, Mama." She nodded sadly and puckered her lips as she always did since we weren't allowed to kiss her.

That was the last time I saw my mother except at the grave. My father came to the funeral with two white men who stood on each side of him all the time. There were people crying all around us. My grandmother kept squeezing me and moaning. I saw my father try to cover his face but one of the men said something and he stood up stiffly after that. I didn't cry, because my mother seemed to look happier, more rested than I had ever seen her. For some reason, I was glad she was dead. I think maybe, except for us, she was too.

I was nine, my sister five. It was not until ten years later that I saw my father again.

We sat on opposite sides of a screen and talked into telephones. I had come there to tell him that in spite of my beginning, I had made it. I was nineteen, and a radioman in the U. S. Coast Guard, ready to fight and die for my country. There had been something mysterious about his smile.

"I'm proud of you, boy," he said. "You're a real man. You know I volunteered for the front lines too, but they turned me down."

We don't want you, I thought, we're not criminals, we're honest, strong. Then I looked again at this thief, this "Loaf-of-bread gunman" as the papers had tagged him. He had taken five loaves of bread, along with twelve dollars. Suddenly I could not stay there condemning this man, my father. It seemed such a waste, this magnificently strong man sitting there, his tremendous chest barely moving, hands resting quietly. He seemed to have accepted his fate and yet I felt as though he were talking to me, his whole being showering torrents of words about me.

"Be careful, boy, there are so many ways to fail, the pitfall sometimes seems to be the easiest way out. Beware of my future, for you must continue, you must live. You must, for in you are all the dreams of my nights, all the ambitions of my days."

A bell rang and we stood up and a man pointed me toward à heavy door. I looked back, and saw him standing easy, hands at his side, so very calm, yet my mind filled to overflowing with the many things he had not said. It was to be ten years before he walked again as a free man, that is, as a physically free man.

I remember an earlier time, an earlier chapter of my growing up. I remember the first time my mother said we were taking lunch to my father's job. We had been down to the welfare line and I had stood with her, our feet burning against the hot pavement, and slowly moved forward in the sun. Years later I stood in chow lines over half of the world, but no desert, no burning deck was as hot as that day.

At last we reached the man sitting at the desk and my mother handed him the book of stamps. She smiled, a weak almost timid smile, as he checked her name and thumbed her to the food line.

As we headed home, my wagon was loaded with cans of corned beef, powdered milk, powdered eggs, and white margarine that she would later color yellow to look like butter.

At home we made sandwiches and off we went to my father's job, to take him his lunch. I pulled my sister along in my wagon, a Red Flyer.

It was to be a picnic, a celebration really, my father's new job.

I remember the wagon did not have a tongue or handle but only a rope with which I pulled it wobbling along. We were excited, my sister and I, as we left our district of dirt streets and unpaved sidewalks and began to make our way along roads called boulevards and malls we had never had occasion to travel. The streets themselves were fascinating, so different. They were twice as wide, and there were exotic trees along the sidewalks and lo and behold trees down the center of the street as far as I could see and then we turned the corner and before us stretched an overwhelming sight. An overhead highway was being built. Columns rose to staggering heights, bulldozers thrust what seemed to me mountains of dirt before them, and hundreds, no thousands of men seemed to be crawling like ants hurrying from one point to another. Cranes lifted nets of steel and laid them in rows on the crushed rock.

I stared in awe at important-looking white men in metal hats, carrying rolls of papers which they intermittently studied, then pointing into space at what to me seemed only emptiness.

And then I saw my father. He sat among fifty other black men, all surrounded by great boulders marked with red paint. They all held steel chisels with which they cut along the marked lines. They would strike a certain point and the boulder would split into smaller pieces and as we approached there was a silence around them except for the pinging of the hammer against the chisel. In all the noise it was a lonely sound, futile, lost, oppressive. My father seemed to be concentrating, his tremendous arm whipping the air. He was stripped to the waist, black muscles popping sweat, goggled eyes for the metal and stone only. We stood there, the three of us, my mother, my sister, and I, and watched my father work for us, and as he conquered the huge boulder my chest filled with pride. Each stroke shouted for all the world to hear: This is my family and I love them! No one can tell me this was the act of a lazy man.

Suddenly a white man walked up and blew a whistle and the black men all looked up and stopped working. My father glanced over at me, grinned and winked. He was glistening with sweat, the smell strong and powerful. He dropped his big hand on my shoulder and guided me to a large boulder.

"Hey, boy, you see me beat that thing to bits? This one's next," he said, indicating the one that shaded us from the sun. "I'll pound it to gravel by nightfall." It was a challenge he expected, he welcomed. That was my lazy, shiftless father.

And then one day they brought him home, his thumb, index, and middle finger gone from his left hand. They sat him in the kitchen chair and mumbled something about carelessness. He sat there for two hours before he answered our pleadings.

"Chain broke, I — I was guiding boulder. I couldn't, I just couldn't get my hand out from under in time — I, goddam it, Jean, they took my fingers off. I layed right there, my hand under the rock, and they nipped them like butchering a hog. Look at my goddam hand."

My mother held him in her arms and talked to him. She spoke softly, so softly my sister and I, standing in the corner, couldn't hear the words, only the soothing softness of her voice.

"Joe, Joe, we can." And then he began to cry like — like I sometimes did when I was hurt deep inside and couldn't do anything about it.

After that there was a change in him. My father had been a fighter.

He had feared no man white or black. I remember the time we were sitting on a streetcar and a woman had forgotten her fare — or maybe she never had any in the first place. Anyway, the driver slammed the doors on her and held her squeezed between them.

My father jumped up, snatched the driver out of the seat, and let the woman out. He and the driver had words that led to battle and Pop knocked the driver down just as a patrolman arrived. The patrolman didn't listen to any of the people that tried to explain what had happened. He just began to swing his night stick at my father's head. It was a mistake. My father hit him once and even today I can see all the people laughing at the funny look on the policeman's face as he staggered back all the way across the street and up against a building, slowly sagging down.

The police wagon arrived with four other policemen and one told him they were going to beat his brains in when they got him downtown.

My pop had laughed then and backed against the building.

"I guess ain't no sense me going peaceable then."

They knocked out all his upper front teeth that day, but as he said later, "Them four white boys will think of me every time they shave."

They finally overpowered him and dragged him, still struggling, to the wagon. One of them kept muttering, "He's one fighting son of a black bitch, he's a fighting son of a bitch."

All the time I hadn't said a word or cried or yelled as they stomped and kicked him. I had shut my eyes and held my lips tightly pressed together and I had done just as he'd always told me.

"You stay out of it, boy, stay real quiet, and when that wagon leaves, you run behind and keep it in sight. If they lose you, you ask someone where the closest police station is — that's where I'll be. You go home and tell your mother."

That's the way he had been before losing his left hand. Afterwards, well, it took a lot from him. He told me one day, laughing and shaking the nub as he called it, "If I'd only had the thumb, just the lousy thumb, I'd have it made."

Gradually he lost the ability to see humor in the nub. I think the whole thing came to a head the night I killed the kitten.

We hadn't had meat or potatoes for over two weeks. Even the grease drippings were gone and my mother was too sick to raise her head from the pillow. So I had gotten the skillet and put it in the open grate. We had two cups of flour so I mixed water with it and poured it into the greasy skillet. I can still recall the coldness of the room on my back and the warmth from the grate on my face as my sister and I knelt and hungrily watched the flour brown.

You know, today my wife marvels at how, no matter what she puts before me, I eat with relish. My children say that I eat very fast. I pray to God they never have to experience the causes of my obsession. But back to the story — the flour finally hardened and I broke a piece for my sister and a piece for my mother and left mine in the skillet on the table.

I took my mother's piece over to the bed and put it in her hand. She didn't move so I raised her hand to her mouth and she began to suck on it. Then I heard my sister scream, "Topsy is eating your food, Junior, Topsy's eating your food!" I turned around to see the cat tearing at my tiny piece of hard dough. I went wild. I leaped across the room and grabbed the kitten by the tail and began slamming her against the wall.

"That's my food," I kept yelling, "my food!" At last I heard my sister screaming, "She's bleeding, you're killing Topsy. Here, here, eat my bread. Please don't kill her."

I stopped, horrified, staring at the limp nothing I now held. It was two weeks later that they got me to speak and that same night my father left the house for the last time. I don't say that what he did was right. No, it most assuredly was wrong. But what I do ask is, what else could he have done? I need an answer quickly, now, today, for I tell you this, my children will not starve, not here, not in this time of millions to foreign countries and fountains to throw tons of water upward to the sky, and nothing to the hungry, thirsty multitudes a stone's throw away.

Will There Be Another Riot in Watts?

No, not as the riot of last summer, not as a spontaneous, frustrated explosive reaction resulting in death indiscriminately. No, this will not happen again, for "the niggers and criminal elements" that fought and died learned their lessons well. They were given well. It is related at night in the quiet of dimly lit garages:

"Man it was close, I mean I was that close to death — let's face it — Charlie can throw too much power for open warfare. We gotta do like those French were doing when we landed over there . . . the underground."

UNDERGROUND has connotations of deliberately planned moves involving the risk of life, the almost ultimate assurance of death.

Private dance-parties where no one dances to the continuous playing of the record that reproduced the sound of light laughter and conversation. Church prayer-meetings with no one on their knees, where no one looks at the Bible, held in reverent hands, but at cold blue steel in hands burning with black fury.

Maps that are covered with pencil marks indicating long-forgotten entrances and rust-covered locks that open silently and iron gates that move on well-oiled hinges; stumbling winos who drink colored water and practice runs past storage tanks that could spray flaming oil miles in all directions; locksmiths who make two keys.

Strangers in ominous garb that walk among us and talk of death as their great reward.

No, there is no shining, wildly bubbling black kettle about to explode, but there is a horrible coldness toward any attempt at compromise. There is open contempt for the peacemakers, and they are warned; you go white, black man, you go first, even before the white man, because you could have told him, you should have made him understand, but you only nodded and smiled and ate the crumbs that he could not hold.

So at this moment it goes on, the white man going on blithely secure in his armies, committing the same, the very same acts, and as he does, these acts are not forgotten or forgiven but are used as powder to load the human guns, and fill the flaming souls until the people are saturated with death and welcome it.

And then — and then, God help us, for a man blind with injustice does not value worldly goods, for themselves alone, and so he will destroy and destroy until the ache in his soul has burned out. . . . No, there will be no riot in Watts; possibly, just possibly, Armageddon.

The Sand-Clock Day

This is the story of my sand-clock day. Every man has a sand-clock day. A turning point, a decisive day. For some it is the road up, sometimes all the way to the top. This was my day. It started good — let's face it, in order to win you've got to have a chance. For some reason I felt I had it made, you know how you get that feeling. This is it, this is that once-in-a-lifetime.

This morning was brisk, baby, I mean cold, you dig . . . and as I sit here I can see that room now. You ever wake up and see your breath steaming from your mouth? You know how it gave you that vigorous feeling? Man, hit the deck and let's fight the world, 'cause today I'm Samson and Delilah's in trouble, baby.

My wife's a sweet tiny thing with all the guts in the world and the sound of her voice is like music to me. Funny, after all these years of creaking floors, rattling windows, and scrambling cockroaches she can just say my name and I'm a bridegroom again. Hey, and you ought to see my kids — I can walk into that bedroom crowded with its rickety beds, secondhand clothes from the Goodwill Store, and someone's patched-up last years' toy, stare down at my children, and I'm "God."

And then (five minutes later) standing ouside the door I am among the animals, scratching, biting, and kicking for survival. Baby, this Los Angeles smog is cold. Maybe I'm getting old, blood getting thin. Hell — thirty-six isn't old, feel more like eighteen right now, but man, if you want to gain some age, try one of these job-hunting expeditions into the frightened, frustrated white man's world. Bring your lunch, and if you're real smart bring your dinner, because it's an all-day trek. Having an appointment for a job is only half the battle 'cause job-hunting in the wide-open spaces ain't like in the city, the Windy City . . . or even old Bean Town. At least there you have rapid transit, speeding underground trains that cross cities in minutes, but not in the west. Man, I swear those buses don't have engines, they got real horses for power, plow horses at that — and it's only time for one job a day, so be right the first time.

I got me a swinging appointment for nine o'clock today, reporter yeh, reporter. I used to be reporter on a newspaper, Yeh! it was a real kick. Okay, suppose it was only a weekly, but you know those were the times I really felt like somebody. Times when with just the right words I have turned the tide for a person really in need. Hey! What I tell you about this city? Forty-one cents to ride three miles, ain't that a gas? And not even a transfer! Look at that bus driver-o — got the nerve to be indignant, like he owned the company. Man, if that so and so makes me miss that other bus. . . . You know a man sure got to be desperate to ride one of these things. Believe me, as soon as I make a good pay I'm buying a car. Yeh, they sure burned around here! You know I look at all this and I remember the burning, the dying, the killing, and I get the shivers, baby. All I can think of, is this what happened to the Jews in Nazi Germany? That's a horrible thought, 'cause if it follows that pattern, baby, we've just begun to die. Yeh, Charlie got him a good-looking car there. You sure got it made, Dad. It's a funny thing that all the movies are always in the center of town.

Where in the hell would Seventh and Hill be down here? The bus information said walk down Fifth to Hill Street. For crying out loud, first the driver's late getting started, now I got almost a two-block walk. Man, this Main Street is rough. Reminds me of the Bowery in New York. Hey, what was the name of that street in Boston? Dover? Dover Street, that's it, skid row itself. Man, you ever look into the future? Take that guy right there for instance — ever project yourself ten, twenty years? It scares you. How many times can a man fail? How many times can his children cry of hunger? How many times before his wife walks out? — and that's all I got, baby, my wife, my kids. Long as she gets up in the morning, smiles at me, and those kids got that house ringing with sound, I'm gonna make it.

Oh, for crying out loud, there's my bus pulling out. Hey, wait a minute. Hey, open those doors. You dirty . . . that lousy, no-good . . . He could have stopped. He could have stopped. Lemme see, where's that paper? "Apply before nine A.M. Writer wanted, man with wide newspaper experience, plus some advertising copywriting, capable of taking over house organ." Maybe I should call and tell them I'll be late, but I can't afford to, I've got just enough to get there and back. They'll hold it for me 'cause I told them I had plenty experience and they were real interested. Must have been or they wouldn't have made an appointment to see me.

Well, a thirty-five at last. How much? Eighty-one cents, damn. Can you imagine all that damn money to get to work?

Wonder what she's carrying in that shopping bag. Probably uniform, shoes, apron. Hey, where you going, girl? You don't have to go to the back of the bus anymore. Hey, old mama there looks like she's had a rough day.

I wonder where he's going? Probably the same deal I am, looking for that job. Look at that frown. He got some sad hard memories. Uh, uh, experienced janitor wanted, 21 or 25, just as I thought. Don't worry, boy, I'm not trying for your job.

I wonder about those physical requirements, hope this weight don't hold me back. 'Course, I already told them about it.

I wonder what time it is. Man, that clock is running around. You mean to tell me we're going on the freeway? Man, it's an hour and fifteen minutes from here. I'm going to have to do some tall running when this thing stops to make it. Come on, driver, swing around her, swing around that woman. That' a boy, get some speed to it. Yeh, but don't wreck us, I want to get there in one piece.

All right, all right, open the door. Let's see, this is the 1800 block. I have to go to 2006. Get to humping. Let's see, what did that clock say? Twenty minutes late. Come on boy, pick it up. Damn bus. That must be the building, heh, 2006. Well, I made it.

I'm Harry Dolan. I have an appointment for the writer's position. Well, that was a nice smile, so everything must be all right. I wonder who the men are in that office behind the window. Sure I know I'm late, but not that late. You mean it's been taken already! You didn't have time to interview anyone else. Okay, I get it. Thanks! Would you please call if anything else comes up? Anything!

Oh, hi! I didn't make out as good as you did, Dad. They just hired somebody else. Man, I need a drink. Naw, I guess I'll let the booze go, got enough problems now. What am I gonna tell my wife? What am I gonna tell my wife?

Well, it's like I said before, every man's got a sand-clock day, a turning point, a decisive event. Some go up, some go down. This was my day. The last grain in the sand-clock.

Crazy Nigger

I just read in the paper that my friend Jakie was dead. It says he went crazy and slaughtered his mother and stepfather, and then committed suicide. Ain't nothing wrong with that report except for the crazy part. Of course, they was nice and said "insane."

Well. Like I said, Jakie was my friend and somebody ought to set the record straight, you see—

Deacon Carter, Jakie, and Maybelle lived next door and their house was the best on the street. They had a hedged fence around their front yard which Deacon Carter evened up every Sunday after morning services. He'd come in from church ahead of everyone. He walked very straight and fast, which kept Jakie running to keep up with him, and by the time the rest of us on the block got home he was already clipping away and she was already chipping away — his wife, Maybelle, that is.

Deacon Carter's job at church was to sort of keep an eye out for the sisters who would get too happy hearing the Lord's word and would begin to shout and stomp around. It seemed that in their getting close to God, they would sometimes break up a lot of the church's furniture or hurt themselves if they weren't controlled. That was Deacon Carter's job, control the sisters. I don't think I mentioned that Deacon Carter was a very handsome man, and had the best tenor in the whole church. When Preacher Davis got to jumping and stomping and preaching Hellfire and Damnation, and Deacon Carter got to humming on those high notes, sometimes there wouldn't be an untrembling woman in that church. For a fact you had to keep a sharp lookout not to get trampled. Some of those sisters, like Miss Fannie Johnson, weighed over two hundred pounds, and if you got caught by a backhand of hers you just better have needed some front bridgework done.

Somehow this sounds funny, I guess it's the way I put it down, but it wasn't, 'cause it was Preacher Davis's preaching and Deacon Carter's tenor voice and the fiery words of the Lord that led directly to Maybelle becoming a whore.

Like I said, she was accusing the deacon of having every woman in the church and believe me I'd watched too, but truthfully not once had I seen him do any more than was necessary to control them sisters. Seemed to me those things were the best things to grab when they got on a rampage. But Maybelle didn't think so.

Feeling them. That's what, right in church before the whole world, you feeling that fat cow and she liking it. Funny thing was Maybelle was the finest woman round, shaped like a brick shithouse and twice as fine. But talk about jealous.

She would go on and on every Sunday. Maybelle cooking and fussing and Deacon Carter humming and trimming and Jakie playing deaf and grinning.

But one Sunday Maybelle came to church alone, that is except for Jakie, and curiously enough none of the sisters got happy that Sunday. As a matter of fact Fanny Johnson didn't come either. Never crossed no one's mind anything was wrong until Maybelle came running out the house later that day, screaming all over the neighborhood.

"Oh, Lord, he done left me. I don't want to live no more."

She had a bottle of ammonia in her hand and a note in the other. She began drinking, gagging and drinking. I turned right around and headed for the kitchen, grabbed a bottle of milk and ran for Maybelle.

She was screaming now, her voice filled with fear and agony, blood pumping from her mouth.

"Drink it," I shouted, but she couldn't hold the bottle to her mouth. I grabbed a handful of hair and forced her head back and slopped the milk down her throat.

"Ma, Jakie," I called. "Ma, get the doc. Maybelle trying kill herself."

By now everybody on the street had crowded around the hedges staring at Maybelle twisting and turning on the ground.

"Git them niggers out of here," I yells at nobody in particular. 'Cause they naturally had their minds on Maybelle's nakedness which kept showing, her kicking and jerking and carrying on like that.

Anyway Doc got there and gave her a shot.

"Probably saved her voice, boy," he said to me. "That milk was good thinking."

Later that evening me and Jakie found the note Deacon Carter had left.

"You take the whole kit and kiboodle, I can't stand your mouth another Sunday. You was right about one thing, Fanny shore do want me, and I want her too. See you in church. Charles."

After that Maybelle stopped going to church, and every Sunday when we got back from church she'd be sitting on the front porch with some of the "bad niggers" drinking beer. Jakie took to staying more and more over to our house. Seems his mother didn't have to worry about money 'cause Deacon Carter sent a check every Friday. She'd give Jakie a dollar and tell him to go to the picture show, he came to get me and off we'd go.

Then one day this white man drives up and tells Maybelle that Deacon Carter has sold him the house and that she now has to pay rent or move. That Friday no check arrives. Me and Jakie didn't get to go the movies either. We just sat around listening to Maybelle cussing Deacon Carter one minute and crying the next.

Then one Saturday morning this slick-haired, real smart dresser comes strolling out of Jakie's house, stood out on the porch and stretched and sighed, and all the time he had this silly smirk on his face. Pretty soon Jakie came out but he wasn't smiling and as he passed, the sharpie rubbed Jakie's head and handed him a dollar. Jakie came over.

"Wanta go to the show?"

"Sure."

We started down Success Avenue.

"Hey," I said at last. "Who's the guy?"

"My father," Jakie said softly.

I stared at him. "Your father? But —"

He whirled on me, tears in his eyes. "My father, my father, that's what I said, that's what I was told to say, that's what I said, my father."

I nodded. "OK, Jakie, OK."

We went to the show but it just wasn't the day for Roy Rogers. It took us longer to get home that day than ever before and when we turned the corner we could see Mr. Sharpie sitting on the porch, just swinging away and whistling.

"How was the movie, son?" Sharpie asked.

Jakie mumbled something.

"What?" Sharpie said. "Speak up, boy, when your daddy talks to you."

It wasn't long before lots of men began dropping by to see Sharpie, and Jakie began to sleep with me, and all hours of the night you could hear the clink of bottles and loud voices and more and more Maybelle's voice would come through the night air.

"There's too many, Eddie, I'm tired, there's too many, too many."

Then Sharpie's voice would thunder and there would be a sound of someone getting hit and Jakie lying beside me would tremble and I lay there like I was asleep listening to the horrible night sounds.

Jakie all of a sudden took a real interest in church. He went to Sunday School, morning services, afternoon and evening services.

"What's gotten into you, Jakie?" I said. "You getting ready to die?"

He didn't answer, just shook his head. But there he was every Sunday all day long, right in church.

In the meantime a couple of Eddie's friends had moved in and now Maybelle began to leave the house every day 'bout six, all dressed up fit to bury.

"Gotta job, Jakie, everything's gonna be all right," she told him one day and after that Jakie quit going to church.

"You know," he told me, "there *is* a God. I know."

"What do you mean, you know, you crazy Jakie?"

He didn't say anymore, just sort of laughed.

It was almost six months later Jakie and I both were celebrating our sixteenth birthdays and with five dollars apiece were headed into town to the movie when Sharpie stopped us.

"You boys need better action than a movie show. Come with me."

It was the first time he'd even let us near his Cadillac car let alone get in. He stopped in front of this house.

"Well, boys, time you learned the facts of life."

We looked at each other. He must be crazy thinking we didn't know 'bout girls. We walked in and stopped, staring opened-mouthed. There must have been twenty women were sitting 'round, young, old, some dressed, some almost naked. They didn't even look at us, but stood up and began to walk around us like they were modeling their undies or something. I sneaked a glance at Jakie, he was grinning and come to think of it, so was I. All I could think of was that saying, "All that meat and no potatoes!"

"All right boys, through shopping? Which you want?"

I ain't saying nothing. I'm waiting for Jakie and he's waiting for me.

Sharpie laughs, says, "All right, all right, look. You go in there, and you go in there."

He gave me a shove into a dark room and this lady's voice says,

"Hi, handsome, come here."

About half an hour later as I'm going out the door, she turns the light on and gives me a kiss. "Don't forget, Baby Face, ask for Ginger next time."

I nod, grinning from ear to ear. Sharpie's waiting when I come out.

"Well, well," he giggles.

"Wow!" I says. "Thanks a million."

"Yeh, yeh," he giggles, watching the other door.

I see the light come on under the door, I hear Jakie moan, then there is a long loud scream and Jakie comes running out, puking all over the place, Maybelle right behind him, screaming and begging Jakie to wait. But he takes off up the street, Maybelle naked as a jaybird right behind him, and Sharpie, right behind her, laughing like a hyena. Jakie kept right on past the house and that was the last time I saw him alive. I don't know, but I think I figure like Jakie did. It was time to end that blood line. He did the best he could. He only missed Deacon Carter and Fanny. I'm going to get them for him. I wonder if the newspapers will say I'm a crazy nigger — I mean insane — too?

Losers Weepers

CAST

Petey	Insurance Man	Mother
Mary	Sgt. Taylor	Neighbor Woman
Grandmother	Father	Welfare Worker

Patrolman, 2 Ambulance Attendants, 3 Pedestrians, Baby Mary

ACT I

Exterior of Edge house — Day

The frame house of Mrs. Edge, grandmother of Petey, 14, and Mary, 7. It is a dull smoggy day. There is an old stuffed chair on the front porch. The front yard is neat but barren of grass except for a desperate attempt to grow some flowers. Petey is working with some garden tools. He comes around to the side fence and dumps some weeds in the vacant lot next to the house. Then he heads toward the backyard. As he passes the window on the left side of the house the Grandmother hurls a wet towel at him. Petey dodges.

GRANDMOTHER (*From window*): Don't know what you cleaning up for. It don't change nothing.

Petey glares at Grandmother, throws the towel back at her, and walks on toward backyard. Mary is pulling her doll in a broken wagon.

MARY: Petey, what's wrong with Grandmother?

PETEY: She's nuts, you know that.

MARY: Yeah, Petey, but why does she always pick on you?

PETEY: 'Cause she knows I know the truth, her lying about everything. She got plenty of money. I saw it.

He stops quickly as the door opens and the Grandmother comes limping out. She is carrying a bag of wet clothes to be hung up.

GRANDMOTHER (*To Mary*): Here, child, hang these up. This ain't no time to be playing, not with that killer on the loose. (*A car horn sounds*) Who's there?

INSURANCE MAN (*Approaching from car*): It's me, Mrs. Edge, the Insurance man.

GRANDMOTHER: Insurance man? What name?

INSURANCE MAN (*Getting out of car*): It's Collins, Mr. Edge. I came for the three seventy-six you owe me.

GRANDMOTHER: Oh yeh, yeh. Lord, have mercy, more money. How's a body going to make it? I'll get your money.

She enters the house as the Insurance man sits heavily into a battered chair. The children glance at him as he lights a cigar.

GRANDMOTHER'S VOICE: I don't have a penny to my name, just my check from my poor husband's insurance, that's barely enough. (*Exiting from house*) I don't know how long I'll be able to keep up these policies. Rent going up, food so high, a body just don't know what to do.

INSURANCE MAN: Yes, ma'am, it's getting harder all the time. 'Course we got to look out for the young ones. You know what happened to Mrs. Kemp's daughter. She was on the sidewalk and that car still hit her. Just think what would have happened if she hadn't been insured with my company. You know we pay the biggest dividend, pay it if it's only a arm or a leg. Lord knows I hope nothing happens but with those two kids to think of — and you not getting any younger. By the way, Mrs. Edge, I understand you're taking glycerine tablets.

GRANDMOTHER: Don't worry about me, long as I got my pills.

INSURANCE MAN (*Enjoying his bad joke*): You know what I always say — a pill a day keeps the doctor away. But *I'll* be back.

By now he has got his money and leaves. Grandmother goes back to rubbing her arm.

MARY: Is it *that* bad, Grandma? What's wrong?

GRANDMOTHER: They's turning that killer loose, that's what. That cold-blooded child-murdering killer loose on the world.

Petey is just staring, the hate plain in his eyes.

MARY: Who, Grandmother?

GRANDMOTHER: Your father, that's who. He'll murder us all in our beds.

PETEY: He ain't no killer.

GRANDMOTHER: How do you know, how do you know? He robbed that telephone-office payroll, didn't he? He used a gun. You snot-nose brat. (*Grabbing Petey's face*) Look here, just like your father. A born killer. Look at that nose way up in the air.

PETEY: What's wrong with my nose?

GRANDMOTHER: Proud, boy, that's what he called himself. Look at you, always putting on airs, just like him talking 'bout how someday he be something. Something, huh! Every good job he ever got ended up being fired for sassing. Him and his high falutin' ways. Huh! Your grandfather was one of the best janitors in this city. He even got that smart-aleck father of yours on a job, but he said he wanted something better. And your poor mama — she died soon after you was born, child, dragging herself off to work. And even as she worked, he argued at her all the time, all the time.

Interior of Edge house — Day
Flashback to Grandmother's house seven years earlier. Little Petey enters from back door and comes into kitchen. Father is heating baby bottle in saucepan and holding baby. He can see Mother in bedroom as she hurries through her dressing, spraying hair, putting lipstick on, checking stockings. Grandmother is lying on living room couch as Father enters the bedroom.

FATHER (*To Mother*): It don't have to be that tight — I can see everything you got. You might as well be naked.

MOTHER: I know it's too tight, Pete, but Mr. Stein told me to either wear it this way or leave.

FATHER: Leave then. (*He slams the bedroom door*) Leave! You ain't no hustler, you ain't gonna' be no hustler. And I ain't no pimp.

MOTHER: Pete, we got to do *something*. You ain't working.

FATHER: I know I ain't working. So that's your excuse. Sure it's all my fault. I'm ready to work. (*He holds his hands up*) I'm ready — where is the work? It's all my fault! I'm a no-good lazy bum like your mother says, right? (*He pulls at dress, trying to rip it off*) You ain't going out of here like that.

MOTHER (*Embracing him*): Pete, please, I love you. *You,* Pete. If I had to walk naked in that place, it wouldn't make no difference. You're my husband and no matter what happens it's you I'm proud of.

She starts to cough, harshly. He holds her tightly until coughing subsides.

FATHER: That cough! Where's your medicine? Why don't you take your medicine?

MOTHER: I'm out of it, Pete. I, I was gonna' pick it up tonight after I got paid —

FATHER (*Quietly*): You're right as usual, Beautiful. It just kind of gets me, you know. I know those guys down at that bar. I can hear them now — "Hey girl, you pearl . . ."

She stops him by kissing him fiercely. He responds and she pushes away and runs into the living room. She kisses Grandmother and exits.

GRANDMOTHER (*Calling after her*): Take care of yourself, Baby — your baby-sitter won't.

The baby begins to cry.

GRANDMOTHER (*To Father*): Hey, you! You! Ain't that baby food ready yet?

Father grimaces at the question as Grandmother gets up and leans against the bedroom door.

GRANDMOTHER: Will you take care of that child? You at least oughta be able to do that.

FATHER: Shut up, woman.

GRANDMOTHER: You're the mother, ain't you? Well then, feed her. (*She giggles*) Let's see you *nurse* her.

FATHER: I'm telling you, leave me and my children alone. Get out. Get out of here.

GRANDMOTHER: You don't tell me what to do in my house. I'm the master here, not you.

Father jumps to his feet and looms over Grandmother.

GRANDMOTHER: You don't scare me — I've known *men*. Her father was a man. He worked and supported us every day of his life, so don't jump at me, Boy. Go to that work-farm like a man would.

FATHER: I ain't digging weeds for no handouts.

GRANDMOTHER: No, you'd rather work my daughter to death. Huh, you phoney — you great big bull-jiving phoney. Living off a sick woman, sleeping in an old woman's bed. *My* bed. You gutless part of a man!

Father almost hits her, then begins to throw clothes from dressers, shoes from under bed, etc., onto the bedspread.

GRANDMOTHER: Ha! Same old routine! (*Then realizing he is serious*) Are you crazy, man? Have you gone stark raving mad?

FATHER: I'm telling you, Mrs. Edge, if you don't get out of my way, I'll, I'll —

He starts to gather the children and head for the front door.

GRANDMOTHER: Where you taking my daughter's children?

FATHER: Home. We're going home. I don't care what you say, we're going home.

GRANDMOTHER: Mason Street, that pigsty?

FATHER: It's mine. We'll survive.

GRANDMOTHER: You ain't taking these poor children out of here.

She grabs Mary, runs to the bedroom, and locks door.

FATHER: Open up, woman. So help me, I'll kick it in. (*There is no response*) Old woman, so help me.

He kicks open door to bedroom and grabs Mary.

GRANDMOTHER: No, don't take them children — NO!

FATHER: Come on, Boy, let's go home.

They walk out as Grandmother staggers after them in the doorway.

GRANDMOTHER: I'll see you in jail! I'll have the police on you, Pete Marshall, you'll see. You'll never support them, never. You ain't got nothing and never will have. You'll kill 'em all if I let you. You'll kill 'em all!

Father and children reach the street as Grandmother slumps in the doorway.

Exterior of Edge house — Day

We are back in the present — in the backyard. Petey starts climbing a telephone pole to scan the streets for his father's return.

GRANDMOTHER: She died soon after he took you away. She was murdered. He killed her just as surely as if he held a gun to her breast and blowed her heart out.

PETEY: You lie, Grandmother, you lie. He said he loved her. I read it. I read it in the letter you keep hid in your drawer.

GRANDMOTHER: So you'd fight for him, huh? Defend him against me, me who raised you for eight years. Now he's coming home, expecting to get you children back. I *know* it. I *feel* it. But he won't. You belong to me, legal — and if he makes trouble . . . he's crazy, you know. He'll do anything. He tried to kill me at the trial. He screamed and cursed me. (*Grabbing her heart*) My pills . . .

She rushes into house clutching her heart with both hands. Petey climbs down from the pole and begins to burn some trash he has collected. Mary follows.

PETEY: Wow! Old goat-face really blew her stack, huh?

MARY: You know, Petey, we don't even know what happened. I mean, did he really kill our mother?

PETEY: You saw the letter, didn't you? What did he say? He begged Grandmother to write him, he even asked how Mom was. Jeepers, he didn't even know when she died.

MARY: I wonder what he's like, Petey. He can't have done what she says. He wouldn't kill her, would he?

PETEY: I don't know, but if she ever hits me again, just once more I'll — I'll kill her. I'll wait until she goes to sleep and stick a butcher knife in her throat. I'll punch her in the heart and make her have a real heart attack. She don't know what it's like to be sick. I mean dying sick — like, like Mama . . .

Interior of shack — Day

Flashback: The Shack. Mother comes in. The coughs are racking her body. She falls across the bed exhausted as Little Petey (aged 7) *runs to her.*

PETEY: Mama, Mama, are you sick? You need help, I'll get Mrs. Crosby.

Mother makes a supreme effort, sits up, and manages to smile.

MOTHER: I'm okay, Petey. Where's your father, where's your father?

PETEY: He left. He'll be right back. He — just went up the street.

She tries to get to her feet but weakly falls back on the bed.

MOTHER: Bring me the baby, Petey.

The boy carries little Mary from the crib.

PETEY: Here, Mama. Here's Mary. She's all right. I just fed her. She's all right.

She takes baby, and with great effort lowers herself and cuddles her.

MOTHER: What will happen to you? Who'll take my children? (*Then after a moment*) Petey, guess what I want?

PETEY: A Delicious apple?

MOTHER: Right, go to the store for me.

Petey nods, takes money she hands him, and starts out. Mother begins to cough; she turns away from the baby.

MOTHER: And Petey, you were right. On your way tell Mrs. Crosby to come over.

PETEY: Okay, Mama.

He goes. She tries to cuddle baby but hardly has the strength to hold her.

Exterior. Railroad tracks — Day

A freight train rushes past. It cuts Petey off from the house. He peers under the train toward the shack. His POV to an ambulance and a woman on the porch holding the screaming baby. A stretcher is brought out with the Mother on it. The train finally passes and Petey races to the ambulance.

PETEY: Mama, Mama!

MOTHER (*Almost incoherently*): Petey, tell your father . . . Ask your grandmother . . .

The doors close and ambulance pulls away. Petey walks up to neighbor woman holding baby at the shack door.

PETEY: My sister, I want my sister.

NEIGHBOR WOMAN: Petey, your mother asked me to help until your father comes.

PETEY (*Snatching baby from woman*): You let go, we don't need any help. My pop will be home soon. We don't need you.

Neighbor woman is a little frightened to challenge him and walks away. Petey takes baby into house.

Interior. Shack — Night. Later that evening.

Petey is trying to feed the baby. Father comes bursting in. There is a gun in one hand and a paper bag in the other. He sees the boy is awake and hides the gun.

FATHER: Where's your mother, boy? How many times I gotta' tell her not to work no double shift. (*He laughs nervously*) She don't have to work anymore, no sir. Don't be scared, boy, don't worry about a thing.

PETEY: Mom's sick. She's in the hospital.

As Petey gets off bed he knocks a model airplane to the floor, picks it up, and continues to carry it throughout rest of scene.

FATHER: The hospital. Oh, my God! Did the doctor say anything? Did he say she was — ? I've got to call, Petey. You wait right here. It ain't bad, honest, son. Mama's going to be all right. Honest. I'm gonna call, Pete. Yeh, call. I'm going to the corner and call.

Father starts for door then stops and hands the paper bag to Petey.

FATHER: You be sure and hold onto this. If I don't get back, it'll take care of all of you.

He rushes out. Petey looks after him.

Exterior. Street — Night

There is a telephone booth. Father runs to telephone and dials.

FATHER: Give me emergency. . . . Did you pick up a sick woman? I dunno what ambulance. Yeh, my wife, a colored woman. Marshall — Gloria Marshall, yeh, that's right. Colored . . . Black. She's a black woman, *a black woman* . . . Is she, is she —

The lights of a police car sweep the telephone booth. Father glances up, drops receiver, and runs. Petey at window watches Father running, chased by two policemen.

PETEY'S VOICE: But he kept on going. I shivered when I heard a rat run across the floor, and got into bed. Daddy, I kept moaning, please don't leave us alone. After awhile I began to say to myself, we don't need you, we don't need you, and as I fell asleep it echoed in my brain. We don't need anyone, *we don't need anyone.*

ACT II

Interior of Edge house — Day

Petey is washing a window. Mary is out on the porch. A police car pulls up and a tall white plainclothesman approaches — Sgt. Taylor. Grandmother hurries out, followed by Petey.

SGT. TAYLOR: He got out at ten o'clock, Mrs. Edge. He'll probably come right here.

GRANDMOTHER: I don't want any trouble with that killer.

SGT. TAYLOR: No, no, Mrs. Edge, he's been a model prisoner. You'll hardly know the creature — that violent temper is dead now.

GRANDMOTHER: You mean he ain't bragging now, huh? Not stamping and shoutin' about being human, huh? Damn willing to crawl now. Ha, I'll bet he bragged plenty up there.

SGT. TAYLOR: Well, well, you might say it's broken. Of course, after a little time outside he'll be all right. I'd say all he'll crave is peace and quiet.

GRANDMOTHER: Well, I'm ready. Guess he ain't so smart now, huh? He mess with me, he won't see these kids at all. Lord Jesus, thank you for bringing mine enemy to me on his knees.

SGT. TAYLOR: Yeh, okay, Mrs. Edge. If you need us, you know the number. I'll be cruising this area.

He goes. Grandmother sits down in her chair. Petey begins nervously tearing out more weeds. From afar we see the figure of the father approaching.

GRANDMOTHER (*To children*): You two get back in the house.

At last he is there. He reaches into his pocket and brings out a crumpled letter. The kids peek around the door, wide-eyed.

GRANDMOTHER (*As she reads letter and looks up*): Well, what do you want? This ain't no official letter, it's just a suggestion from the warden.

She enters house.

Interior of Edge house — Day

Father enters living room. He goes toward the children but they move away shyly.

FATHER: Mrs. Edge, they . . . they explained that you had legally adopted my children, but, well, the Warden thought, he . . .

GRANDMOTHER: He thought what? That I would welcome you with wide-open arms, that I would kiss you and forgive the murderer of my daughter?

FATHER (*Evenly*): Don't ever say that again, old woman. . . . (*He stops, relaxes slowly, fighting for control*) Seven years is a long time, Mrs. Edge, even for a stick-up.

GRANDMOTHER: My daughter will be dead longer, just for loving you.

FATHER: What happened, Mrs. Edge? Seven years, seven years. Not a letter, not a visit. What's been going on? Well, let's forget all that. Let's be fair with each other. How's it really been? Did that money help see you all through?

GRANDMOTHER: You, you didn't leave nothing.

FATHER: Thirteen thousand dollars.

GRANDMOTHER: You didn't leave *nothing.*

FATHER: I left thirteen thousand dollars.

GRANDMOTHER (*Ignoring this*): She should have divorced you like I told her to do. You weren't no husband. I told her all she had to do was divorce you and I'd take her back. Begging to be your wife, her spitting blood at every breath. Dying right there.

Dying — and all she could think of was a no-account like you. I told her to ask the Lord for forgiveness for sins before Him and to come on home to Jesus.

FATHER: I want my kids, Mrs. Edge. I served my time and I want to start fresh. I need my kids. I learned things up there. I read and read. It's just that I was ahead of my time. Now . . . Now these black men are standing tall and telling the world like it really is. That's what Pete Jr. is gonna do. I'll show him now.

From the bedroom Petey and Mary listen.

MARY: He *does* love us. He is right there saying it.

PETEY: Yeah, but he didn't say he loved us. He said he *needed* us.

GRANDMOTHER: How would you support them? That boy eats like a horse and Mary needs a woman now more than ever. You got some money?

FATHER: I got strong hands, I learned a craft. I can repair shoes. But I don't need to — you have money that belongs to me.

GRANDMOTHER: Repair shoes — *shine* shoes would be your line, or better, why not steal them? You get out of here, Peter Marshall, you get the hell out of here. Sergeant Taylor, he said if you got smart to call him.

FATHER: It can't be right, Mrs. Edge, for you to have my children. I thought about it real hard. I tried to tell myself you'd be fair but deep inside I knowed it wouldn't be. It's simple, if you couldn't let your daughter love me, how could you let her children love me?

He has been jabbing Grandmother in chest with his finger and with almost each sentence increased the force of his blows until he has backed her across the room. When she reaches the wall she starts to fight back.

GRANDMOTHER: I'll send you back to prison, on the next train smoking. You, you killer. You murderer. Oh, my heart, my heart — Lord have mercy, my heart. (*She falls*) Get, get my pills, my pills. . . .

The Father bends over trying to help, then jumps up calling Petey.

FATHER: Petey, Petey, where's your grandmother's pills?

PETEY: Pills? I don't know about no pills.

FATHER: They'll blame me, boy. Hurry, get the pills. (*He grabs Petey and begins shaking him*) Where are they? *Where are they?*

Petey says nothing. Father begins ransacking the dresser drawers. Petey stares innocently at Grandmother as she gasps for air.

GRANDMOTHER: Petey, where — where you put my pills?

Petey looks off toward Father, hesitating.

FATHER (*Desperately*): I can't find them, Mrs. Edge. Where are they? Please don't die. I'll be blamed. Where, where?

She tries to talk but can't. She raises her hand, points inside, and dies. Father drops to her side, moaning. Petey quietly goes into the kitchen and picks up the pills from the sink.

FATHER: They'll blame me, they'll blame me.

He looks up. Petey is standing there holding the pills.

PETEY: They were right on the sink. You just didn't look for them.

Father stares at Petey in disbelief. Then he gently carries the body to the bed. The children retreat to the living room.

FATHER (*Entering*): All right, boy, you think you're tough, huh?

PETEY: I'm tough, I don't need no gun either. And if I did I'd use it right. That's why you went to jail. You were stupid.

FATHER: I never killed nobody.

MARY (*To Father*): How come you went to jail?

FATHER: For you. You were hungry.

PETEY: You had a gun, that's why you went to jail.

MARY: Grandma says you worked Mama to death.

Father turns from one to the other, trying to reach them, explain the unexplainable.

FATHER: Petey, Mary, I tried to make it, but boy, I didn't have it. You know what I mean. I couldn't learn to crawl and — and, boy, it ain't hard, it ain't hard. All I had to do was learn to say, Yes sir. Move when I was told to. Stop when I was told to. I just couldn't do it. I was too soft. I thought I was tough too, but I was a weaklin'. You don't understand me, boy?

PETEY: You shoulda' done what you had to, only you couldn't, so you — you left us all alone. But, but, we didn't need you, *never.*

Father suddenly picks up a beer bottle, smashes it, and holds the jagged neck menacingly.

FATHER: Suppose, boy, I said I'm going to kill the two of you. What would you do?

PETEY: I'd kill you.

Father moves forward an inch.

FATHER: Right answer, but it takes more than words for you to kill, boy. Especially now your grandmother's dead. You need me.

Petey pushes Mary behind him.

PETEY: I understand more than you think. I understand I *don't* need you. You're weak and you've always been weak. You killed my mother with it, you killed Grandmother with it, and now you want to suck on us until we're dead too. (*He stops and gathers from deep inside of him all the long memories of hate*) Lay down and die, old man — *you are finished.*

Father sinks to a chair beside them.

FATHER: Yeh, okay, yeh, but understand why, boy. I — I been scared so long I don't know how to be brave, but you, you be brave and if it takes fighting your own people like me, then fight. If it takes dying, then die, but don't you be following in my footsteps 'cause I ain't *got* any.

Father goes into bedroom and dials the phone.

FATHER: Hello, give me the Third Precinct Station. . . . Hello, name's Pete Marshall. Tell Sergeant Taylor the old lady's dead. Huh? What difference it make? Come get me. Hey, you better bring somebody for the kids, too. Thank you.

FATHER (*Reentering living room*) Boy, I was going to try and hand you the world like a split nut. I think I could have done it. Now. I could have done it. Well, that's the way the Black Jacks, huh?

Exterior of Edge house — Day

There is the squeal of brakes and Sgt. Taylor and a uniformed patrolman come up to porch.

SGT. TAYLOR: All right, Marshall, come on out, hands in the air. You know the routine.

Father comes onto porch.

FATHER: Sure, Taylor, you got no trouble with me.

Taylor puts cuffs on Father as children stand watching from door. Taylor looks at the children.

SGT. TAYLOR: You kids don't have to worry. Mrs. Reese is on her way over.

The children stare. Taylor walks into house and we hear him dial. The phone call plays over the faces of the children on the porch.

SGT. TAYLOR'S VOICE: Look, get over here — looks like homicide. I don't know. Yeh, the wagon. Okay, Monty.

Sgt. Taylor hangs up and begins to check the body. The children approach the toy chest near the living room window. The welfare worker and another plainclothesman enter as Sgt. Taylor reenters the living room.

SGT. TAYLOR: Hello, Mrs. Reese. Take care of the kids. (*To plainclothesman*) The body's in there.

Sgt. Taylor exits.

Petey is holding his model airplane and Mary her doll.

WELFARE WORKER: Is that all you children need? Just toys?

PETEY (*To Mary*): That's all we need, huh Mary? We don't need nobody. We learned. Ain't gonna be no weeper like — like he was either.

He nods toward the police car outside. Welfare worker shrugs and exits to bedroom. Petey slowly opens plane and shows Mary hundred-dollar bills jammed tightly inside.

PETEY: Not as long as I got this — thirteen thousand dollars. We don't need nobody. Nobody. It's finders keepers.

MARY (*Singsong*): Finders keepers — Losers weepers.

Exterior of Edge house — Day

The street and porch. The children walk out with Mrs. Reese just as police car prepares to leave. Father raises his handcuffed hands in salute but Petey and Mary don't respond. They get into Mrs. Reese's car.

SGT. TAYLOR: You didn't give them much chance for life, did you? Some legacy.

FATHER: Legacy, legacy. Didn't you see what they can do?

SGT. TAYLOR: But who's going to get all that hate out of them?

FATHER: That's the problem.

Father and Sgt. Taylor get into car, which drives off, followed by Mrs. Reese's car. At the intersection across the railroad tracks, the two cars separate and finally both are lost in the city.

ALVIN A. SAXON, Jr., who frequently uses the pen name "Ojenke," is in his early twenties. A native of Watts, he joined the Writers' Workshop at the Watts Happening Coffee House in the summer of 1966. He says: "Some men satisfy their longings for a better world by escapism, some by defeatism, and some by coming to grips and defining these terms of existence responsible for man's conditions. The latter is my job as a writer." Mr. Saxon finished high school in Watts and is now attending junior college in Los Angeles.

Morality

1.

The apostle Paul, who interjected woman
into himself and became etherized,
floated on the pebbled streets
preaching a hermaphroditic morality.

Oh, homogenous Paul from the village of the Essenes,
did you not comprehend it all: the road,
the terrible divination?
Now you lie amongst the willows — putrid flesh.
And what of your children, and your children's children?

2.

I remember it well, Dalia —
The day I suggested a day of love
and you took refuge in your mother's words —
in the folded tresses enveloping her moral knees.
You even pretended puritanical ascendency
And in short you were morally scared.

Indictment

Come let us mock the blackman
killing the yellowman and dying
for the whiteman — but not for himself.

Mock Mock Mock

Praise the brave warrior with gold
and silver and bronze ornating his chest —
snuffed out the ephemeral life of the sibling
in swaddling clothing held like some treasure
in the mother's tearstained arms.

Mock Mock Mock

After the enemy was beaten
a saint's voice was heard
amidst the warbled cries of the dying
and the wounded: "Come ye

repent thy sins
The Lord in his mercy
shall forgive."

Mock Mock Mock

I
grow w
e
ar
y — weary of soliloquizing
I with my Socratic knowledge
shall not mock thee oh Lord —
for I am thy greatest mockery.

Black Power

1.

There shall be no more songs
of soft magnolias that blow
like aromatic winds through southern vales,
no more praises of daffodils chattering
the wind's fluttering tune —
and no eulogies of red, red roses
that fall like blood from heavy vines.

Black Orpheus calls, his lyre piercing
the dark solitude of a Hadean world:
Come O Ebony-hued Eurydice, he beckons,
he shan't look back — the lesson has
been well learned.

2.

There have been despondent days
and long nights of insomnia —
but your voice, sweet Eurydice,
was like some Nigerian wind that
blew softly through the water willows,
your lips like manna — they were
good for my soul;

and your hands that caressed my
worn limbs like a profound unction
and when I laid my head, dense with
woeful memories, on your cloud breast
I slept deep and tranquil and
the day held no insurmountable fears
for me.

To Mr. Charles and Sister Annie

1. Africa

Bilious thoughts
wrapped in sugared words
fall like butterfly melodies
on ignorant ears.

A flask of liquid fantasy
makes pink skins and needled propositions
seem like platonic virtue;
Dahomey Warriors,
ring-nostriled Ibos,
rubber-jointed Watusis,
bleak-eyed Mandingos.

Fiery-limbed bare-bosomed black women,
befuddle-eyed children,
form a panoramic bacchanal
observed by frozen blue eyes
colder than the tempered shackles
held like serpents in snow hands.

2. Atlantic

Neptune's cradle
heedless of cries a long way from home,
rocked "Good Ship Jesus"
(powered by fifty indigo-veined black arms)
like river Styx's good ferry to Hades.

"Good Ship Jesus": whites sing
prayer hymns — defiant blacks
hang like anchors
and chandeliers in Neptune's mansion.

3. America

Black beasts of burden;
profane words spat out of the mouth of the world.
Seared by Apollo's impartial ray.
(Charles: you know what that puny jew
nailed to crossed oaks, with his
honey words, would mean to despondent
bleak-eyed black people
whose heads are worth 50¢: "Wasn't
one chain enough?")

We have removed the cataract
from history's impartial eye:
we weep for our mothers:
your tearless eyes saw only
sirens of black beautiful thighs.
We grow enraged for our copper-wombed mothers
you phallic "motherfuckers" see only as
ebony-hued aphrodisiacs.
We weep for our fathers, blank-eyed,
like consent trapped in bars of silence.
With history's impartial eyes, your words
have no sugar and are but snowballs falling
on our ice-blocked hearts.

4. America

Continuous America's
tresses of gold
fall like sunlight
on Mrs. Ann's
oceanic eyes — her eyes reach
out from tempestuous heart

wrapped in sand-tanned skin
enveloping sinewy, lithe
body of noble limbs.
Her lighthouse teeth
and lips make
fluid vowels that
lure like mermaids,
which mean:
"White cunt shall
silence *Black Power*."

Watts

1.

From what great sleep
lightning jumps from an amber sky
causing famine,
assassinating tin people and whole grass-blades?

Senile edifices crying like lumberjacks: "Timber!"
Streets of dwellings wrapped in cellophane
of negligence,
where old wine-winded wisemen in oversized coats
and baggy trousers soliloquize a jungle futility.
And a baby warbles a milk-dry cry
to a mother's wiry ear who sits ice-eyed
with frozen pain like icicles in her heart.

What great sleep,
resonant with nightmares,
causes a man to awaken gap-eyed?

2.

Diogenes came with a burning lamp
searching for honest men, but his beautiful light
fell only upon the shadow people
and those who found meaning in the penumbral days
meted out in marijuana's fantasy
and the half-bliss of the prostitute's bed.

Socrates came with nebulous knowledge
to make a liar of the Oracle of Delphi,
but found only
schoolrooms of metal and wood carvings
and those who escape into
some kind of intoxicant — running from
some too-true truth.

Against what false fantasy
the children ball on their golden slides,
bouncing balls, and putty clay —
and Socrates, horrid-eyed, gulped the hemlock
while weeping Diogenes hurled his flame
to the barren soil.

JEANNE TAYLOR's father, a native Californian, was a successful drummer during the depression jazz era. Her mother had attended Southern University in Louisiana and had taught school to rural Negro children in that state before coming North. Jeanne Taylor, who was born in 1934 in Los Angeles, began writing in junior high school, and soon became editor of both her school paper and yearbook. She earned a degree at Los Angeles City College in 1954, where she prepared herself for a career as a social worker-probation officer. She studied for another year at the University of Southern California, then dropped out to get a job. Married in 1955, she is the mother of three children. For the past ten years she has worked off and on in the Department of Employment and with the Division of Highways. Her interest in writing returned after her children were born. She has been a member of Budd Schulberg's Writers' Workshop since May, 1966, and serves as secretary of its Council.

Listen, America, Ebony Middle-Class Is Talking

Black, I am today
And black will ever be . . .

Yes, black and conceived during the cold, hungry nights of the depression, reared in the money-plentiful years of World War II, and now, at thirty years plus, we live in the year of the too-near disastrous future. Thus far we have spent a life on earth not worthy of the historians' note. The half-completed cycle of our lives has been one big waste of time! We speak not for black Watts or black Harlem. We talk of coffee-cream Leimert Park, Inglewood, Morningside Park, Baldwin Hills, Altadena, and Pasadena, where the lawns are green and the latest Chevrolet and Ford stand glistening in the drive, and the bills are barely paid each month and bankruptcy seems the sure way out. Where husband drinks more and more and is building as fine an arrest record as his black brother who steals and is considered the decadent result of the ghetto. Where a woman treads a lonely middle path, hated by her "poor" east-side cousin who can afford but one cheap, new dress all year, and by the doctor or lawyer's wife, who doesn't want her fantasy black-white world invaded. It's the envied Utopia we cry about, where young Mother and Father detest each other a little more each year, and sex has become a grotesque imitation of affection because what was revered during the romantic years of courtship is gone. Now the offspring are indulged lavishly because love has to be given to someone, something. Ours is a cry that says: hate us not for trying to rise up and above the man-made hell on earth; do not reject us because our cars and homes were bought with hard physical labor and not with the mind of an intellectual. Our hearts also strangle on the despair of racial injustice and the anguish of hopeless dreams that we've been told should never have been embraced. Our hands search desperately for the grip of happiness, love, and understanding. When you see us smile in our poised, self-confident way, stop and look a little closer. The corners of our mouths are really turned down. The tears are there, mingled with the mascara. And when we laugh, listen — is there not a sob in our voice?

So the next time we meet on the highway to wherever, smile our way. We breathe, we bleed, we die too!

The House on Mettler Street

913 Mettler Street is just another part of the scenery. The once-gray wooden steps sag hellward in a pathetic plea, unheeded. A yellow and white banister flouts an ageless paint-peeled decor. Three boards of the wood porch are missing and the others squeak from decay. The rusted screen door has a new aluminum patch at the bottom, an antithesis in metal.

STOP

the frenzied scrubbing, and STARE at the missing lumber on the porch.

GLANCE

at the clock. ELEVEN-THIRTY. The meeting is four and a half hours into the future.

The bucket of water is grimy with dirt-grease from the living-room baseboards. If someone would only help. Who cares?

AUNT SISSY?

Aunt Sissy has a new beau with a new Buick. Aunt Sissy is turning fifty. She's just lost twenty pounds and bought a wig.

MAMA?

Mama tries. She tries to wash the clothes and cook the evening meals. Then she gets tired, and she starts thinking about Papa: bones decaying in a five-year grave. Handsome face: large mouth; even, snowy teeth; twitching nose when angry; teary eyes when happy. No more. Strong face: covered with worms; covered with dirt; covered with grass; covered with flowers placed there on Memorial Day, Father's Day, All Souls Day, SEPTEMBER TENTH, "Papa's Day."

MAMA THINKING ABOUT PAPA.

Mama, drinking a beer. Mama, hurrying around the corner to Mel's liquor store. Mama, hiding a flask of Mel's cheapest in her purse: to the bedroom; get a book; turn on the television. Mama asleep; the next day sick.

THROW

the wash towel into the murky water. SIT, back on up-turned heels,

REMEMBERING. The last meeting was at Polly Smite's house on Irwindale Road. A large white stucco with rose-pink shutters at the windows. A lawn, green and even, not a spot of sunburn; walnut hi-fi in the living room, long golden sectional around the wall, trays of brown and white sandwiches, frosted glasses of champagne punch, coffee black and strong, bridge in the paneled den.

DART

for the kitchen, OPEN the freezer. Two fifths of sherry into the refrigerator, next to the cheese and luncheon-meat plates, each piece laid out symetrically, design elegant, original.

QUICKLY

to the bread box. Three packages of butter-flake rolls, in place. NOW to the serving board; cream and sugar dishes washed twice; dried sparkling.

MOVE

slowly back to the living room. Furniture perfect; the sofa sponged with fabric cleaner, Papa's large chair mended at the side, white dotted swiss curtains blowing at the open windows, candy and nut dishes exactly right on the coffee table, the *Vogue* magazine in view, in a casual belonging-there position.

LOOK UP

as Mama stands at the front door.

"I'm glad you took your little walk around to Mrs. Lawson's house, Mama."

Mrs. Amanda Lawson lives around the corner, down the street from Mel's liquor store.

RELIEF

as Mama reaches the top of the stairs, disappears into her bedroom.

THE TELEPHONE RINGS, Polly Smite can't make it. Sorry!

STARE

at the forgotten note on the telephone table. "Trudy Love, can't make it. Sorry!"

SMILE.

More refreshments for everyone this way.

ONE O'CLOCK. Kitchen mopped; lace cloth ironed, put in place on the polished table; bowl of artificial flowers over the cigarette burn in the middle.

THE TELEPHONE RINGS. "Jess? Hi. Well, I'm having club meeting. Of course I want to go out. Where? Not riding again, I'm tired of seeing the ocean at night. How about dinner and a show? O.K., then, I'll treat."

TIRED,

and missing Papa. Cold glass of Schlitz, always good for the weary female.

TWO-THIRTY. Time for a bath and the Saturday afternoon movie. Water runs in the tub; THE TELEPHONE RINGS. Suzanne, can't make it. Sorry!

WHO THE HELL IS COMING?

Sign of the cross; Act of Contrition, SHAME! SHAME! SHAME!

THREE-THIRTY. "Come in, Janice. Glad you're here."

FOUR-FIFTEEN. "Ah! here's Marriane and Lucille. Welcome. Didn't think we'd get a quorum. Can't stay? Why? Sure I understand. Sit down, Lucille. See you at work, Marriane."

FIVE O'CLOCK. "Bridge? Sure, why not with a dummy, REALLY TWO.

REFLECT

as Janice's black crepe dress goes down the broken steps. Next month, odds on a crowd at her apartment in the Crenshaw Towers.

Mama comes to the top of the stairs.

SMILE.

"Yes, the meeting's all over, Mama. It was just fine! Sure Mama, we're as good as the rest of them. Do take a nap, I'm going out anyway."

WALK

to the table, enough cheese and meat for next week's lunches. Enough wine for Aunt Sissy and her beau.

Enough!

Enough!

Enough, of the house on Mettler Street!

The Stake-Out

Going to Li Chou's is a semi-monthly must, and if you want to be "in" you make the trip with everyone else. Being "in" is important when you are twenty-two, single, and on the minus side of attractive; when you haven't decided if you prefer a warm cup of milk before bedtime to a Scotch on the rocks, or whether blushing is more apropos than the coy knowing smile.

So, you sit at the bar in Li Chou's and watch Chang mix your Mai Tai. The large glass is filled with crushed ice, exotic tropic juices, Bacardi light, Bacardi dark, Anejo, and then topped with "151." Chang's special garnish is last — skewered to a tiny green umbrellaed toothpick are a red cherry, a green cherry, and an orange slice. You smile at Chang. He smiles back. He likes you. You're the sweet kid: soft voice, never profane; skirts the proper length, never too tight; just the right amount of make-up. Never made a pick-up, at least not in Li Chou's. Amy, your girl friend, stirs on the stool next to you. She eyes the Mai Tai, dashes off her Scotch and soda, and tells Chang she wants a Mai Tai too. Amy wants everything, Amy gets everything, Amy is never outdone.

You hear Mama's voice. "Get the hell off that stool. I worked all my life, for this. . . . A tramp!" The words are slurred. Three beers too many. The memory brings a sick sweet taste to your mouth. You loved her. You told her: words, looks, caresses. She never believed. The tears reach the brim of your eyes.

"That's life. . . . That's what all the people say. . . ."

Sinatra's voice, a tap on the shoulder, and the memory, the tears. Mama's gone.

You turn around to Detective Sergeant Fisk's boyish grin. Your legs are weak. If you were standing you'd have to grab for support. You try not to, but the corners of your mouth slowly spread into a shy, ivory smile. Your eyes are at half-mast and the color is in your cheeks. You remember the picture of Detective Sergeant Fisk's wife and three children, all snowy and dark-haired. The boys like their father; the girl, like neither mother or father.

"That's life. . . ."

Sinatra's voice croons on, and without a word you turn back to the bar and the Mai Tai. You want Detective Sergeant Fisk to go away and you want him to stay. When he doesn't move you're angry *and* you're elated. Amy wants Detective Sergeant Fisk to stay. She tells him so. Damn Amy! She wants everything.

Li Chou's is the place. The stake-out. The only anticipated crime, pleasure. Off-duty officers getting stoned, cheating with the office help, having one hell of a good time. In or out of uniform, always men. Big-limbed, square-jawed, crew-cut, trained smiles, perceptive eyes, probing minds. Men. No uniforms now. Just a room full of sportshirts and khaki pants, wind-breakers and pullovers, cashing paychecks, paying old tabs. And the women, single and searching.

The day's eight-hour shift has been incarceration. So close, can't touch; don't look, wink slyly. Hands meet at the passing of reports. Nostrils pick up the scents: Arpège, Chanel #5, White Shoulders, Currier and Ives. Bodies scream silently, minds are obsessed. At Li Chou's it's in the open. Free at last.

Detective Sergeant Fisk's arm is like a boulder on your back and when he opens the palm of his hand and you feel the touch through your blouse, burning your skin, you hear Mama's voice again, ripping the air, "Tramp! Tramp! Tramp!" Mama who never went to church on Sundays but saw that you did, Mama who never explained womanhood, and who said only, when you found out in the teen-agers' curious, probing way, "If you play around with little boys, you'll get into trouble." So for months, you kept away from the neighborhood group. No more hopscotch, hiking, riding bikes.

Detective Sergeant Fisk's hand caresses, and with a slight shrug of your shoulder, you tell him to stop. You play around with big boys, you get into big trouble. You turn around on the stool and he smiles and motions for Chang to set up two more drinks for you and Amy. You shake your head. He applies pressure to your shoulder. Detective Sergeant Fisk is in command and you like it.

Someone puts a coin in the jukebox. Nancy Wilson wails, "I need no soft lights to enchant me, if you'll only grant me . . ."

The door opens, five rookie deputies walk in slowly. First pay night in Li Chou's. Lots of rookies are single, not spoken for. You strain to see as they move to the other end of the bar. Detective Sergeant Fisk shifts, blocks your view. He's jealous. You feel good. There is no need for words. This thing has been between you from the day you first saw each other in the cafeteria. He, surrounded by officers eating late lunch, you and Amy sneaking an extra coffee break. Then silent encounters in the elevators, telling glances, tortured bodies yearning for a touch. Never close until now. Your dreams have captured his face, his form. Only once before have you felt this way. Your senior year in high school. Midsummer. The school's star hurdler. Serene midnight waves, the moist sand warm beneath you. Then days, weeks, months, of loneliness, and in agony the realization that you were the latest conquest, and Mama's voice droning on, "Tramp! Tramp! Tramp!"

Detective Sergeant Fisk is twenty years your senior. Old enough to be your father, young enough to be your lover. He laughs, you shudder. Amy speaks, you close her out. Voices crescendo, the jukebox aproars. Mama's face, wrinkled from decay, shallow from drink, appears in the bar's mirror amid the cordials and liqueurs. "Nice girls don't frequent bad places." Everywhere from the youth center to the ball park was a bad place. "Nice girls stay pure." The thirteen-year-old paperboy, the doctor, the mailman, even the minister—according to Mama all males were lecherous. So there was always just you and Mama. "Mama, I do love you, but . . . No show tonight, Mama's sick. . . . Can't go dancing, Mama needs me." You groan. You look in the mirror again, Mama's gone. Detective Sergeant Fisk puts his mouth to your ear. "Are you all right?" he asks.

You nod. You look at Amy, her head close to the face of a young detective, speaking in subdued tones. You turn around cautiously. The din goes on. Sergeant Fisk, his hand still on your shoulder, is espousing the faults of Cassius Clay with a Negro rookie. You sigh, relieved. If only Mama would stay dead.

How strange was Mama's passing. Alive the end of May, dead the first of June. The night following the funeral, your best sleep in years, and when you awakened, the birds filled the air with song and you were happy. Now a year has passed and the tears are with you all the time . . . and Mama's presence.

You can't remember when she first came back. Was it the New Year's Eve party? You were dancing with Amy's friend from New York, a musician. Your eyes were closed and your body melted into his. You felt a sudden chill and when you opened your eyes Mama frowned from the wall. He wanted to take you home, but you refused. Mama didn't approve. Mama had never come to the old place when you were alone but after you moved in with Amy she was there all the time. She didn't like Amy. Amy drank too much, whored too much, but she was your friend. Mama never liked any of your friends. You couldn't figure out what Mama wanted. Didn't the dead rest? They ought to at least let the living rest.

Detective Sergeant Fisk taps you lightly on the shoulder.

"How about dinner?" he asks.

You hesitate. Mama frowns. You laugh.

"Yes, I'd like dinner," your voice surprises you. It's clear and determined.

Detective Sergeant Fisk kisses the tip of your ear. The corners of Mama's mouth are pulled into a belligerent smirk. You laugh again.

"Happy?" Detective Sergeant Fisk asks.

"Yes."

Li Chou's is the place, and you're "in." Being "in" is important when you are twenty-two, single, and on the minus side of attractive.

JIMMIE SHERMAN joined the Writers' Workshop when it was still meeting at the Westminster Neighborhood Association in January, 1966. He was born in February, 1944, in a project house in Watts, one year after his parents migrated from Texas. He dropped out of school when he was in the eleventh grade and passed through a period of rebellion, becoming what he himself describes as "a hoodlum." Then he joined the Army at the age of seventeen, and was sent to Europe. After the Army, he drifted from one job to another, and was unloading potato trucks just before he joined the unemployed. When the August revolt broke out, he wanted to help. He began to write for a Watts newspaper. He helped organize the Watts Business and Professional Association, and became its secretary. He was serving as publicity director of the Watts Happening Coffee House Board when he wrote the play, *A Ballad from Watts,* which has played successfully at UCLA and other campuses. At present, Jimmie Sherman is teaching in the English Department at the Westminster Association and directing The Theater of Watts. His "Workin' Machine" has been set to music by Steve Allen.

The Workin' Machine

I was workin' real hard on my job one day
When my boss came on the scene.
He said, "Son, go in an' get yo' pay —
An' make way! — for th' workin' machine."

I rolled my eyes — I sho' was sore
My boss he sho' was mean.
He said, "Son, you know I don't need you no more —
You're fired! — 'cause I've got a machine."

Well, I got another job that followin' day
A-workin' harder than you've ever seen —
'Til I heard my boss in a loud voice say
"Look out!" — It was another machine.

Now I'm workin' like a slave an' doin' real fine.
I'm gettin' these floors so clean,
An' I'm hopin' to keep this job of mine
Away! — from th' workin' machine.

The World Is Ready To Explode

A Song for Our Time

You know I'm not assuming
The world is getting smaller:
The population's booming,
We're running out of water.
You'd better tell the Pope
In case he wasn't told —
We're running out of food.
We've got to have control
'Cause the world is ready to explode.

Let's make the world much finer,
And call a truce with China
And then improve the nation —

We'll start with integration.
We'll do away with guns,
Be friends with every nation,
Destroy the atom bombs
And threats and aggravation —
'Cause the world is ready to explode.

We'll tell the men in power
They've only got an hour:
Get rid of all corruption
Before we meet destruction —
'Cause the world is ready to explode.

As Bald As She Could Be

A Song for Any Time

Last night I dreamed
That wig she wore was hair.
I said I dreamed
That wig she wore was hair.
But when I woke this morning
I had a nightmare.

She had a stocking on her head,
Her wig was on the floor,
And her head it was so bald
That I couldn't take no more.

But she's my woman
As bald as she may be,
Yes, she's my woman,
I said, as bald as she may be.
'Cause when she wears that wig
She sho' looks good to me.

Her head may be bald
And look like a bacon rind,

But when she wears that wig,
Man, she sho' does look fine.

Yes, she's my mama,
A fine bald-headed woman is she.
I said, she's my sweet mama.
A fine bald-headed woman is she.

'Cause when she wears that wig,
She's as foxy as can be.
I said, as foxy as can be,
As foxy as can be . . .

My Beard

IS IT STRANGE IS IT FRIGHTENING TO SEE
DOES IT DERANGE OR BRING CHANGE
TO YOUR RULES OF CONFORMITY?

Why do you frown at my beard —
An item so dear to me?
Does it bring to mind
That I'm trying to find
A thing you may never see —
A thing from the past
To which I hold fast
Known as identity?

I'm Here!

I'm here!
At last, I'm here!
Despite the pain, despite the fear,
I'm here!
Here to meet another soul and chat a while
At last. I frown; I cry; I smile —
I'm here!

I'm glad I'm here, despite the bitter pain and fear.
The pain feels good!
It's good I'm here!

Thanks to life, and hail to birth.
I cheer!
At last a life — Mother Earth
I'm here!

Negro History

A ship
A chain
A distant land
A whip
A pain
A white man's hand
A sack
A field
Of cotton balls —
The only things
Grandpa recalls.

Sammy Lee

"You'se a good boy, Sammy Lee,"
Mistah Charley said,
den 'e rubbed an' patted me
ri' chea on dah head.

I grinned an' showed 'em all my teeth,
an' said, "Thank yuh, boss."
I kep' my feelings down beneath
dis happy shinin' gloss.

I nevah lakt dat good-boy stuff
'cause I know whut 'e means . . .
long as I can mop an' buff

an' cept a plate of beans,
long as I say "Yass'm boss,"
an' make lak um in joy
wit' dis happy shinin' gloss
den — um a good boy!

This Is the Home of My Fathers

This is the home of my fathers.
They who helped to win this land
They've conquered the fields of your fathers
With a strong, black helping hand
In chains they've suffered the pains of a whip
And the strenuous work of a slave
In protest I've cried:
You're hurting my pride
When you claim what they worked for, you gave!

This is the home of my fathers.
In all of your wars they have died
In every battle they've risked their lives
And for what? — For freedom denied
They've toiled and strained with muscle and heart
Their bodies all covered with sweat
And with sad weary eyes,
They protested the lies
That stated, "We give what you get."

I am the son of my fathers.
I deserve what they never got
That's a chance to excel
In the things I do well
Without being hanged or shot.

This is the home of my fathers.
Soon it will be of my sons.
I hope by that time
They'll be able to climb —
For oppression could lead them to guns.

Race Compliments

Black Man,
You're wise, joyful, and nice.
Yellow Man,
You're good, with good advice.
Red Man,
You're as good as you were in the past.
White Man —
    You're last!

GUADALUPE DE SAAVEDRA, the son of Mexican migratory workers, was born in January, 1936, in the southernmost part of Texas. His earliest schooling was in a Catholic parochial school. In the sixth grade he won second prize in an essay contest and decided to become a writer. After grade school, de Saavedra entered a seminary to study for the priesthood, but left after a year when he was told he did not have a "vocation." For a while he wandered through the Midwest, "bumming from job to job," then joined the Marine Corps. When he left military service he became an insurance salesman, but decided again to go back to college and become a writer. Five days before registration his wife ran off with another man, and he felt his life was shattered. After an anguished and aimless time he went to a Buddhist retreat and began picking up the pieces. In the summer of 1966 he joined the Watts Writers' Workshop, which, he says, "has given me a reason for living." He is now a regular contributing member.

To Save a Tear

I remember it well. Was it only yesterday? On a cold, chilly Sunday morning in the Panhandle cotton country, a migrant Mexican worker and his son sat on a curb enjoying corn on the cob. It had been a long six-mile walk just to attend church, and now there was the long walk back. The boy was bewildered: he didn't understand why his father's eyes were watery, why he was sniffling as if he might be crying. All he wanted to know was why everyone else at church wore suits and ties and pretty dresses while they wore bleach-stained jeans and faded shirts and worn-out shoes.

The boy didn't know, I didn't know. He didn't understand, I didn't understand. But the boy learned, I learned. Then I knew that this wasn't the equality that Washington had fought for or that Lincoln had sacrificed his life to achieve. I vowed then to find a way to fight all wrongs that exist in the world, to tear down the barrier between those that have and those that are denied the opportunity to attain. Since then, I have chosen as my weapon the sword of expression. This sword, forged in the sweet sweat and blood of blacks, whites, yellows, and in-betweens, can only be honed on the stone of knowledge. This arm will draw strength in the achievement of academic degrees. You may say, "These are bitter words," and you are right. They are bitter words bent on the destruction of all intolerance, hatred, violence, discrimination, and greed.

Maybe then another father will not have to shed tears in silence because he has no answer when his son asks, "Why do other people wear suits and ties and pretty dresses, and we wear bleach-stained jeans and faded shirts and worn-out shoes?"

Jealousy

I could strangle the wind
for flowing gently
through your hair.
I could put out the sun

for daring to lay
its hand upon you.
I could drown all raindrops
for beating so much
on your skin.
I could harness all space
that envelops every step
that you take.
I could burn the time
that caresses you
as you live.

The Law

Smoldering huts.
Towering city against the sky.
Lifeless.
America on the move.
No green.
Make our country beautiful!
Black silence.
Central Park in the spring.
Wailing wind.
Comical hit on Broadway.
Barbecued flesh.
"Pass the gravy."
Life passes on.

Brief Thought before Dawn

The sun has not risen yet
But the day has begun.
Many times this back will bend
Before this day is done.
"Stoop labor."

The Shoe Shine

Mister, how'sa 'bout a shine?
Gee, Mister, only ten cents
'sa all,
Bes' shine all o' New O'leans
Das fer shore, Mister.

Ain't no nigger
Shine black like dat befo'.
Lawdy, boss, a whol' quarter
Tank you, I'se shore tanks yo', boss.
I shore tanks yo', boss.

That's right, boss,
I sure thank you.
You and all your lily-white brothers.
You don't see it, boss,
But your damn vanity
Is putting me through school.

Someday you'll know
But you won't like it
Because things are going to change.
So let me say it once more.

I shore tanks yo', boss.

What Is

There is no truth,
just words.
There is no love,
just lovers.
There is no hell,
just life.
There is no death,
just peace.

Suppression

In death, so still
Unnoticed
This thing
I, annoyed:
The buzzing of freedom
Flight of happiness.
Hasty trial
No defense
No jury.
"Guilty one
Stand up
Hear your fate.
Death.
Now.
It cannot wait."
This hand
Mine.
Crushing blow
The last flutter
Then
down, down, down
The fall.
Hooray!
It
has paid.
This hand
Raised
The victor
The all-powerful.
Who among the weak
Will dare the hand
That justice metes?
A-a-ah, peace
Golden peace
Empty golden peace
Blasphemous peace
Foundation strong
Carcasses

Those that disagreed.
There rot the wings.

It dared be free
Dared be happy
While I slept.
It dared intrude
Disturb my slumber
It had to die:
The fly.

Existence

Grin, fight, kick, joke —
It's the only way to fly.
Smile, stab, pat, strike
Before he looks my way.
Cry, stick, tear, steal —
The means are justified.
Crush, rise, heel crack
It's grown too big
And it must die.

How else could be successful
A person such as I?

The Jewel

A jewel was mine.
I lost it in the
Slimy, filthy gutters of neglect.

Now I wander
Aimlessly, searching.

Finding it, I vow
To make it brighter
Than all others.

JOHNIE SCOTT was born in Cheyenne, Wyoming, in May of 1948. His father came to Watts at the time of the Korean war and Johnie grew up in Watts and went to school there. He has the distinction of being the first young man from his community ever to be accepted in an Ivy League college. After a troubled year at Harvard, he won a scholarship to Stanford University. Joining the Writers' Workshop in the Spring of 1966, he was one of the original "Angry Voices Of Watts" on the NBC-TV Special. During the past summer he has been teaching a course in Contemporary Literature at Douglass House. He tells his own story in the essay, "The Coming of the Hoodlum," which follows. Essays and poems by Johnie Scott have appeared in *Harper's, Time, Scholastic, Pageant,* and other magazines.

The Coming of the Hoodlum

The coming of the Hoodlum was not an entirely unpremeditated affair. Characters within characters took part: Harvard, Watts, and I. It was in the form of a journey, a traveling from the teeming black heart of Los Angeles, Watts, to the pulse of America's intellectual showplace, Harvard: a journey that took only a year in which to begin the gradual eroding away of all former attitudes toward life: an experience that carried its pilgrim beyond his concepts of educational, racial, and social attitudes, that was to find at the culmination of that eventful year's passage a new, albeit embittered and disenchanted, man where before there had been but a child of promise.

At the war's end, the Hoodlum was born: 1948, in Cheyenne County Memorial Hospital. The month of May, of May and sunshine, of a world finally breathing again, of the ending of the spilling of blood on the land, on the birth of a new generation, on the coming of the nuclear bomb, and the passing of a collective hysteria that had produced the bloodiest holocaust in mortal history.

The war's end had found his father, our father, father of the Hoodlum, a soldier awaiting his leave orders, a Negro who had left the South after a painful youth of his own: a son who had to leave school in the fifth grade, the Old South, deepest Lousiana, picking cotton so that a family might survive: a son of sharecroppers and former slaves, a man who longed to be free, free of the bonds all Southern Negroes felt, free to work where he loved — he got his leave orders, his discharge, honorably, all the returning heroes of the war got honorable discharges and all war veterans were called heroes. From Cheyenne to the South to Los Angeles: from the war to the Old South to the West: from death to birth to chance: but then, all men felt a new promise in the air — children were being born, I was born, the Hoodlum was born, the War Babies all were born. Not born into happiness, but into hope, some of the hope to be disillusioned, some of the hope to be fulfilled: the growing years of the child born in a country hospital were to be spent in the teeming ghetto of black folk, Southern emigrants, a dozen dialects, to be known as Watts: its old name, the name of history, was Mudtown.

When Father first brought me to Watts, he had found work in an airplane plant: North American Aircraft: the Korean war, a newer war, going on, the old veterans now sheetmetal workers and engineers while younger men went on to die: Negroes flooding Los Angeles and other western towns, in search of these jobs that took Negroes. He had been fortunate, had saved his money, had bought a small wooden frame house: worked night shifts and, come the light of day, was out in the streets looking for more work, more money, had to have it, the family was growing larger: soon there were two children, three children, four, then five, then six.

In the meanwhile, the wooden structure caught fire and burned completely down. His dreams burned down with it — we moved into the housing projects, the old Jordan Downs Housing Projects. Roaches carpeted the floor at night, a black floor that moved up and down and around the walls, if one woke in the middle of the night to see this shifting blackness in the blackness moving inevitably a scream would escape the lips: we learned to live with them, however; in time man learns to adjust to anything, anyone, any fear, even the fear of insects, the fear of filth: that is, if man wants to live.

Those years in the "old" projects, for newer ones were built late in the 1950's, were changing years, full of growth as Watts grew and the city grew. Negroes continued to come into Los Angeles, Negroes continued to look for those jobs in the West: some, my father, were laid off, others were hired, then fired, more came in their place: it was a cycle, as complete a cycle as one could hope. The ghetto had become more than roaches, or buildings that stank both day and night, more than the oppressive summer heat that left us rasping for breath along with the flies that zipped in and out of the houses — the ghetto had become the people. It was the people: their wishes, their dreams, their forgotten homes, their hopes, starved and starving hopes, and the coming of the bitterness. In this world, a world of darkness, churches were built. Into this world was I born, a half-complete angel.

Those years saw the scars come, scars from fights. Fights that took in neighbors, roaches, broken bottles, brickbats, saw gangs chase people blocks, saw men hop fences six feet tall in one bound, saw bricks barely miss bashing skulls in, saw knives, saw the erection of the churches, saw the night, and the darkness, and the unlit streets: these were the lightless streets, streets that saw bar-b-que joints like Page's on 103rd and Grape, that saw a person's mother get her purse snatched at night if she walked home without a stick in her hand: to become a man and know that there is not that much happiness in the world: to know that you can cry because you have grown old in such a short span of time.

You see police beat people on the streets, in their cars; you hear the mothers cursing the police, calling them "White Crackers!"; you wonder in confusement, What are these words? and then you see the skins: all the white skins clothed in black, all the shiny badges: association of forms, the white skins become the black uniforms, Police, and the voices, the curses, the People — your People, dark as you, fathers and mothers, friends.

And just as suddenly, your consciousness expands. Poverty is not just withered bodies, flesh lost in weeks of hunger, but something else; as an inner Presence, poverty is far greater and menacing. The Spirit of Christmas To Come leading Scrooge before a dead Tiny Tim. Or, something else; more personal — The Poverty had led *you* back in time to your childhood. All of the voices were the voices of friends — a comradery within Watts.

To have a father carried from his home, you the Watcher and the child, away for questioning: you wonder and you see, the handcuffs, memories of the police on television handcuffing the bad guys: the Law and the wrong-doing: again, white versus colored: if the beginning of racism didn't set in by then, it only took the isolation to come, isolation from the white world: the streets and Us against the markets, the cars, the dealers, the other world, Them. We learned, fought off fear against, the white boys, going to the Opera on public school excursions: seeking culture, and found it — found it one's own balled hand smashing against a face you would never see because you had never seen it: smashing out against a blind prejudice: the orphan if you were taken for what you were: wanting to be loved, but in the middle of an unnamed world, alone. I ran out of the house crying, but ran into my neighbors: out in their yards, listening — there never was privacy in a housing project.

But somehow, out of wanting a place into which I could withdraw, I found a refuge in books: I would read, would go to the old library by myself, seven years old: a walk that took me past savage dogs, saw me running by some of the yards with rotting wood fences: on into the quiet, the book: would read of a Round Table, and could see myself in a land where honor was upheld, where men were as free as their pride would carry them.

Would it matter that our Hoodlum could look back on those years and think of how he stood on streetcorners like everyone else; that taunts flowed as swiftly from his mouth when someone could be seen carrying books home from school, or going to the library to do some homework? He didn't think so. That is why, during those years, the beginning of a cleavage began to be felt within himself: a strange and troubling turmoil, born out of the chaos that refused to be shaped in the image of education: a world that refused any sort of understanding, brutal and brutalized, the feelings of the rejected: a time when life came to a standstill for him as he surveyed the great emptiness of his own heart, dissatisfied with the answers streets would whisper into his ears — no less dissatisfied with the chalkboards of the schools, where numbers remained numbers and never became a thought more: while his thoughts sank into memories, wishes.

A cleavage was born that would be nourished by the bitter spirit of the ghetto even though our Hoodlum tried to hide this tear from the eyes of all: include Mother and Father, who soon were to break apart as so many of the neighbors had broken apart: who soon were to become numbers that remained numbers, statistics in the files of the divorce courts and the long rows of Vital Statistics in the newspapers. The pulse of the nation beat swiftly, but not as swiftly as that young heart racing even further into the Hell that was to come. It was a Hell that would see blood flow, his own, and those dear to him — a Hell that would see disputes rise, a family divide against itself and send each member out flying into the streets of that world. Was it any wonder that he sought refuge in books? Was it any wonder that his spirit grew ever more divided? There existed truth, it could be found in the world if only he became a part of it. All that could be found in books were dreams, high and full of mystery. But he wanted dreams.

And so he entered school, the alienated. Alienated out of his own frustration, that longing to resolve the incoherent patterns of a world in which all intemperate attitudes might survive: from ultraracism to Uncle Tomism, from the fear of God to the police-fearing pimps and petty racketeers. His own resolution was simply to survive: to survive and laugh, for it was sheerly by being able to laugh that the horrors could be compromised, that sanity could be maintained. Mayors and governors entered office and then left office. Nothing changed.

What was Watts like?

The year the Hoodlum (we can forget that name, he was no hoodlum, but his friends were, even though they shared his feelings, what made him different?) was elected president of the student body at his junior high school many things happened: inter-school council meetings were held, speeches given, a girl found raped in a classroom during a lunch break, the accent given to good oral hygiene, a seventh-grade girl stabbing her math teacher seventeen times with a butcher-knife because he called her "stupid." But he survived, as the class dwindled in number from 750 to 550, but on the day of graduation this was said:

> Lives of great men all remind us
> We can make our lives sublime;
> And, departing, leave behind us
> Footprints on the sands of Time.

I *apologize,* Mr. Longfellow.

> Leave Markham knowing you left
> Far more than mere footprints,
> Leave Markham knowing you helped
> Begin a brighter future for us all.

From seventh grade to ninth grade, from 750 to 550, from small children to wide-eyed adolescents. But, three days later, they had all matured: 250 were left, the "largest incoming class in Jordan's history," or so it went according to the head counselor: the following years would see larger classes, to be sure, more babies were born each year, illegitimacy and wedlock both strove to rise higher even as people married younger and lives broke up faster. Had the Hoodlum changed in this time?

Yes. He had learned to feel. He had learned that there was no love in this world. He had learned, three years later, as 97 men and women walked across an auditorium stage to receive diplomas, that of the forgotten and the fallen, of those empty 153 "other" diplomas that were not given, there could be no crying. They had not asked for remorse. Even now, they sat in the audience, among the spectators, silent when the speeches were given, laughing when the clowns tripped over their gowns, crying as a brother finally made it, gone when it was over: gone as surely as Death leaves when faced with an attitude of toughness. For the Hoodlum had grown a shell of toughness, that resisted both the hate of the streets, and the love that he tried, wanted, to release. It would have been futile for him to relate these emotions.

Instead, the toughness grew harder, making communication with him all but impossible. But of what, from where, had this bitterness come? Surely not from the mere presence of failure, from the odor of death! One would have thought that the scene of dying hardened one to the facts of life, but this was a different sort of hardening: you went out for sports, wrote on the school paper, became active in student government, studied diligently. Then, you were the biggest prankster in class, the loudest mouth, the silent antagonist of affairs between student and teacher: when in the streets these conflicts were magnified, distorted, the image of truth was purposely turned inside out, hoping to make the true false in order to make things for oneself more bearable. Inside the soul, the pressure was mounting: the days of waiting in outer offices on disciplinary actions, of hearing teachers pass the rumor that you were a "smart-alecky" kid that could think quickly when it came time for assignments but even more quickly when it came time to lie. You went home with him, saw his mother as she went through her daily motions, trying to make a bearable existence out of living, playing the blues. B. B. King, Blind Lemon Jefferson, Billie Holiday, Charles Brown, the old Lowell Fulsom: sounds from his home and from the streets, no longer from Page and Page's Bar-B-Que Pit, it had burned down in the years before. Nothing had been built there, but then, what had ever been built there. Only roasted meat had been sold, and ice cream on hot summer afternoons, and the sound of music where there would only have been the oppressive stillness of one's own thoughts brooding.

At one time, like most of his friends, the Hoodlum hated school, hated Jordan High especially for what it had done to him: *nothing*. That was the reason for all hatred toward the school: his class read no better than sixth-graders and this showed in its average gradepoint: 1.8, the equal of the bottom fifth of the intellectual cracker barrel. His hatred did not last long, a break came, the big break in his life — accepted into Harvard College, the acme of the East, the springboard of Presidents and businessmen; most of all, the place from which decent homes came: *homes* like they didn't exist in his world. Had he been a brilliant student to be admitted? Not if his grades were looked at — 3.03. Had he exceptionally high college board scores? Not especially — 1096. What had he done in school to earn entrance into a Harvard class which claimed an average I.Q. of 128, was selective enough to pick 1,200 people from over 6,000 applicants from the best schools and training institutes in the world?

Nothing, nothing except survive those years of his childhood. Nothing, nothing except remember what those years were, except make it his purpose to somehow do something about it. Nothing, nothing save start out on a career that soon would see him thrown into an even graver crisis: to decide between one's environment, one's home, and the atmosphere of Academia.

Not too many survived that regimen our Hoodlum went through. He had a friend, a member of the 99th percentile, as sensitive and as introspective as anyone, *a human being like we all are,* who never got past the tenth grade. That friend came to class one day, (a science course handled by a man who doubled as a gym teacher in the high school) with a cigar, puffing away as conspicuously as he could. Asked to put it out, he replied, "No. Not if you have to be my teacher. Not if I have to stay here and 'learn' like everyone else. Because I care. I care enough to not give a damn whether you kick me out of school or not." And he was kicked out. Like so many others were kicked out. For reasons of caring. For reasons of wanting something that was neither at home nor in the school. For reasons that still exist in every school even now. For want of a true friend. For want of love. For reasons incomprehensible to used textbooks and second-rate equipment, reasons that surpassed inadequate school facilities.

It is very simple. Have a sister and have her an unwed mother. Close your eyes, blush with secret shame, hide the secret, live on as though nothing happened. Bury that scar with the other scars. And then, at an airport, pose for pictures as the first Negro to enter Harvard with her and your other sisters. With teachers that did not know her but looked away when looked to for answers why: the pictures were taken, the plane took off, and you sat on the plane remembering the past: "I'm surprised you aren't going to Pomona or Whittier College, or somewhere like that! You could have been something but you talked too much. You could have done something with your life. *I thought you were different from the rest!"*

It is not easy to make a happy world when your diet has been tragedy. The tragedy of having to see how much hate, and being hated, of ignorance, and being unknown, of wanting, and being unwanted, the sheer tragedy of being a human in this world. A stigma if you dare to care: the withdrawing into your soul; the thought of another way of life. The ghetto has a way of reaching into your life just when you think you have climbed to the top of the mountain, and bringing everything crashing down. Sisyphus pushing a rock to the top of the mountain, seeing it roll to the bottom again. Laughing while accepting his fate, walking down again to begin over: this, in the real world, was not a myth or a treatise on why not to take death over a half-emptied bottle of sleeping pills: pill-taking had begun far earlier for so many of us, of Them, of the Others who were not on that jet flying across the country to Cambridge in search of a new life as well as an education. But what was education?

It was not so easily defined. It couldn't be: not if, in the process, one knows that only in rebelling against a system that consciously seeks to stifle the creative instinct one rises to the fore, is regarded by one's equals in that environment as a leader that will never be seen or known or heard over airwaves as the representative. Representative! Of what, and then — why? Why, if being representative meant having as one's constituents aged and aging whores, homosexual preachers whose antics sooner or later hit the presses and, when they did, made an even greater mockery of the Church; what if one's constituents were little half-clothed kids who would never be more than half-clothed throughout life, if they got to be any older, they threw away instinctively the protective shell of insulated education for the more existentialist proposition of freedom Now, or Never! Representative of friends and enemies, of those who had not learned their "ABC's" until the seventh grade, who, when they left school, still read at fourth- and fifth-grade levels yet who could, when asked, make the fastest dollar simply by jacking up a car, taking all four tires, the battery, and selling them at dirt-cheap prices to small garages in and around the neighborhood. You stayed penniless those years not because you had no father, or because your mother was on welfare: you were penniless because you were afraid, afraid of being killed out there on the streets, ashamed of being ashamed if you were caught. You remembered bullets, had seen guns pointed and heard them fired at human beings in your world, had seen men die in the streets and it was not called War by the press.

But you got off that plane. With two suitcases, a shaving kit, an open-flight back home for Christmas, and the determination to be something you had only seen in books. A man in love with his dreams. Was it any wonder, then, that the Hoodlum found it so easy to read Herman Hesse's *Steppenwolf*?:

> I cannot understand or share these joys, though they are within my reach, for which thousands of others strive. On the other hand, what happens to me in my rare hours of bliss, what for me is bliss and life and ecstasy and exaltation, the world in general seeks at most in its imagination; in life it finds it absurd. And in fact, if the world is right, if this music of the cafes, these mass enjoyments and Americanized men who are pleased with so little are right, then I am wrong, I am crazy. I am in truth the Steppenwolf that I often call myself; that beast astray who finds neither home nor joy nor nourishment in a world that is strange and incomprehensible to him.

For him, for that Hoodlum, it had been with a near-attitude of revenge that he had walked into the offices of Jordan High, when he had shown each one the letters of acceptance from different schools, had shown them all and had announced his intentions of attending Harvard: and then had come home, had sat with friends who were both awe-stricken and now, in the face of this turn of events, respectful: a distance was growing between the Hoodlum and his world, a distance that soon was to become as marked as that cleavage within his own soul, the division between the ugliness of reality and the bliss of his own imaginations, his wildest dreams for the future. Unless a person fights back with all he has and believes in, the social and academic world of the school system in the ghetto will crush him. But, the fight within our Hoodlum became distorted — transfigured; it was now a short-lived revenge. And, in this especial, bitter cup of emptiness, of tightly wound despair, he knew his own truth — he had found no solace in a sneering attitude, only wanting again to let them know that there existed within each man such a temper of life that, with its own drive, it could surmount the obstacles, it could climb the mountain.

It *had* to climb the mountain for it was the fear of dying lonely, without a soul around, that pushed, that inspired the fearful drive: strange, but during the summer which preceded the Harvard adventure, there was no inkling really of what was to come up, of what the intellectual challenge would be: nor, of how the Harvard *Crimson* would run articles on the stiff competition the freshmen offered upperclassmen in studies, of the new vitality in the class, of its expanding representation of the masses, nor of how his mind would look once he left, a year later. All of that was forgotten, just as all thoughts of the future were forgotten: put aside, the attention was given to parties held in honor of him, held in honor of his achievements, to the beaches where he went to sit and stare at the sand, the sound of the waters flooding into his ears, his mind, his eyes closed. The scent of new life was like a long hungered-for resurrection of the spirit—the total mood was one of enjoyment within the Now, within the real senses of the present, for time had come to a standstill and all that the eye could conceive and comprehend was there before it. Much plainer than the nose of Cyrano's face. But then, that nose caused Cyrano no end of grief, it was the cause of his blushings, his stammerings when faced with the reality of his existence. Eugene O'Neill had said that "stammering is the native eloquence of us fog people." And this tonguetied Hoodlum tried to break out of that habit, as fiercely as he had been reared to break habits.

He sought out his father, going into the heart of south Los Angeles, for reasons why he should continue to live, though that purpose was hidden under another guise: he was worried about the pregnancy of his sister, her being left stranded in the world after bravely venturing out on her own to sample it, her rude shock at being discovered without knowledge of refuges within herself so that she was left marooned on a sea of leering faces. For three hours that conversation lasted. It spoke of the draft, of what the Army had meant to him as he sought out purpose in life. It spoke of how lonely a man can be who has no home to call his own, no family to call his own: though his children come to see him, he is not theirs, not like "Ozzie and Harriet and David and Rickey," not like singing stars or glamour queens divorcing one husband and picking up another one. As his father said, "I wouldn't marry a woman for her money. She'd have to be a little more than pretty, too. She'd have to understand some of the facts about life."

But the Hoodlum did not want to understand some of the facts of life. He wanted to see where there was some justification for these facts, and so the conversation ended as suddenly as it had begun, for the mind of the man had closed and it trailed off again.

His eyes opened again and he was in Boston. He was in Harvard Square, in the Old Commons, the day bright and the opening of school still three days off. Thoughts reeled in of childhood and growing up. The sight of Mama waving good-bye. My sisters laughing. Irvin's crooked grin concealing his devilish heart. Mr. Anderson and Mrs.

Trotter, former high school teachers and friends. Both of them, standing there beneath the plane, so small and yet, so BIG. Watts was just as big as they were. Where was everybody? But then, he wasn't lost. He was in Harvard Square, away from ties he had always hated. He had begun to wonder why he was here, who he was, most of all, why Harvard had let someone with the mark of the ghetto, with the sign of the outcast, into its ivied walls. It was as though Cain had slipped unawares into the Garden of Eden again, but this was a Cain that did not know what his crime was, nor where he was, but only that he did not belong here: neither Harvard, nor Watts would ever be personal worlds for him, and yet they were, because he lived within them.

Now there had been those along the way who sought to look after him. People like Christopher Wadsworth, Senior Advisor at Harvard, and Dr. Dana Cotton, member of the Admissions staff. To him, all of eighteen years old, much of what he saw and felt inspired fear: fear as the voices of the past came into his ears, voices that had predicted failure along the route toward self, voices that never stopped singing in his ear: the voices of the Serpent, the man who wore so much clothing until his body could not be seen and yet who, with but a single question, three words, could disrupt all of his life. *Who are you?* The fear was not of Harvard, but of Watts: a much stronger force than books. He could sit down in dining halls, he could talk with any of a number of people, he could try to study. And then, his sister's face floated across the pages. Here, and then gone. But he could not articulate. He only stammered before the judges, his advisors, these kindly men who sat in on him when he came to them for help: for a help that could not be named, a help that welled up from the bottom of his being, a need that had been there for so long until it was becoming painfully obvious that there could be no life inside of that world. No life was in education if that life had to be shared with the voices of a dead past—a past of Death, whose presence never failed to make itself felt. A presence so overpowering as to draw tears when he sat in his room, isolated, and played the muted trumpet of Miles Davis, played "It Never Entered My Mind," and then turned his gaze outward, into Harvard Yard, into tradition, and history, into all that he had ever read of as a young child striving to find values in life: and could not see because he was blind.

Hello, Mr. Wadsworth, I understand you want to see me?

Yes, I do. How are things here at Harvard for you?

Oh. They're all right, I guess.

Like the way they've been treating you here?

Yes. Everything's all right, I guess. It's an all right place. It hasn't done anything wrong to me I can think of.

Guess it's kind of different from Watts, eh?

Yes. It is a little different from Watts.

How's that?

Well, it ain't anything you can put your finger on. It's like, well, it's like this is a new life, a different place, with different people. It's the kind of thing I expected (seeing surprise on his face), so I don't feel out of place in the sense of running into prejudice.

But then, conversations always ran through those currents for him: he sought to express the difference. It would have been easy to say that he *felt* two different people within him, but he was afraid that someone might overhear and call him crazy. For expressing fears. But this wasn't the simple case, it went much deeper, much further, than an alienation from Harvard society.

Ghettoes are built within the mind, and in one part of the Hoodlum's mind he was *black,* which meant apart from all that is white and stands for white, which meant the faces and opinions of his former friends, those that now were in Watts, behind him and yet in front of him, in front of his face as he sat and talked with Wadsworth: while there was its opposite, that part which had seen the humanity of all men because it had seen the humanity within itself, and known that love could be if only men dedicated their minds to liberation. But to express this was difficult. He would slow down in his speech, some of his Cambridge comrades noticed an overly drawn-out drawl, while at the same time injecting a hatred of white society, a hatred that carried itself into his living quarters. There, walking in late at night from drunken sprees, he found his two white roommates listening to Bach, Mozart.

What is this Mozart *shit?* he would holler, and then, striding to the record player, place atop it jazz albums that were freedom songs: the songs of protest, that spoke out against all the injustices, that were in themselves reflective of the black position, of the position of Watts and black life as it had to reach out for breath in an all-white, and all-dominated superstructure largely unknown to it. A super-society that was predicated upon a foundation of books, of knowledge: the same books that had fed the Hoodlum's soul at night when he was a child. His mind would roll back: there was Dale and Jack and J. C., finally reading *Baldwin* after I've been through King Arthur and so much more of other things until it's almost pitiful. But then, he would be glad at the same time, glad to see the hunger for truth in the faces of others. He had begun to wonder to himself about the possibility of communication amongst peers. That Christmas of 1964, he sat in an old garage in Watts, talking with some of his former childmates, deep in the depth of Harvard and what Veritas might mean for Us.

That's right! They have got so much to read, to see, to understand! IT'S LIKE THEY GOT THE POWER AND THEY DON'T REALLY KNOW IT BUT AS LONG AS WE SIT HERE TALKING ABOUT IT INSTEAD OF GETTING UP AND DOING SOMETHING WE GONNA ALWAYS BE ON THE BOTTOM, FELLAS! Yes, he had styled himself a revolutionary. He had majored in African History, would sortie and frequent with the foreign exchange-students. Much of what they said and much of their humor he couldn't understand. But he could sense their own feeling of desolation in this great community, a sense of aloneness that was very much within him, too, and as homing devices are attracted to one another, he came to know of those customs. But he was also a Negro, a fact he couldn't, didn't, escape from: he did sort out other Negroes on the campus and together they formed a group which centered its interests, aspirations, on a black culture: the scene was established for a black dialogue, meetings were called in which other Negroes of the freshman class discussed racial sorespots on the Cantabrigian scene. Then, though no resolutions were ever reached, they always ended the meetings with firm declarations on the strength of black peoples, of their right to survive, of their pride in themselves as future leaders, and on the beauty of the black woman, a beauty that could not be mared in its sensuality — not even by the stated four-hundred-year rape of Prospero.

That was a year of many changes. From revolutionary, the Hoodlum went to mystic. His religion had become one of Godhood, though it concerned no Christian God. He found himself in his room again many nights, questioning his belief in life. Am I a Muslim? Can I, do I, I know that in *some* ways I hate white people, but then there are some that are all right! I can't be a Muslim! But that doesn't make me an Uncle Tom! It was a term that had come to be feared, as many people were becoming aware of the yet-carpetbagging ghost of Uncle Tom stealing in and out of the nights with caches of cash while whites walked away smiling, thinking communication had been established with *comprehensible* Negroes. But nothing is so reprehensible as an Uncle Tom, or the smug face of the white collar that tells of working for everything he's ever gotten in life. As if life wasn't a struggle in the ghetto, but rather, a mere question of survival! What was the difference? What had Harvard become that he thought like this? He lay on his bed into the waking hours, looking at the sun flood the room, the bed, the body, his mind: standing up, he would shiver with the first cold, and then, smile almost ritualistically. To think that I can be here anyway, be here and be mad and be free! Walking into the Co-Op, he bought records, books, gloves, paper, pencil, letterheads, anything he could buy: he charged it willfully, beyond his allowance, wanted to break himself completely, knew that destruction loomed just ahead but rushed on pell-mell.

There was a continued interest in his plans, his future, his life. Many worked with him. Not much was said in those meetings of what impressions were being made. The talk centered around Harvard, Watts, clothes, studies, anything, in fact, but who was talking to who. And why, in the first place! It should have seemed natural to believe that sincerity surrounded every meeting, that this sincerity provoke a concern in his wishes. But the Hoodlum would not have sensed this, nor would he have responded. His world was too clouded, too filled with the spectres of his world, *that* world which now included Harvard as well as Watts, which began to space time and memories: so that there were times when he was afraid of going home, afraid of going there and finding that he wanted Cambridge instead. The exact fear he had when first arriving of wanting Watts more than he wanted Cambridge. The Hoodlum *knew* that he was changing, in name and form as well as in belief. The Hoodlum was dying, he was fighting, kicking, yes, but he was also dying. And this is why he was so sad. No one is happy, not very happy, when a part of them dies, when a fragment of the past begins to recede into the mists.

To be sure, he had encountered prejudice. But it was a subtle kind unknown even to its perpetrator. He had gone to the B'Nai B'Rith House at Harvard, for example, for a party given there one evening by the Hillel Foundation. The place was packed. Of the group he was with, there were six altogether, four whites and two Negroes, not much in the way of overt attention was paid. But then, as our Hoodlum stood away from even this group, in a corner, watching the people, hearing the sounds of the party, listening to the wonderment in his own eyes, a small, bespectacled Caucasian fellow strode up to him and, there, from the top of a drink, asked, "Do you feel a little uncomfortable here, if you don't mind my asking?"

"Only if you feel uncomfortable." To know that he did not know that I would not know until the morrow that the B'Nai B'Rith was a Jewish Foundation. Or that Jews had suffering in common with *us* Negroes, and that they, too, were meeting injustice in the present world.

There were questions that could not be so easily answered, though: What does *your* father do for a living? No, he wasn't a Civil Service employee. Then, he was not unemployed. He could not answer that question. He did not know the answer. My father is a laborer. The hardest kind of worker, because to hustle in the streets, knock someone in the head and take their money, run away, that would be so much easier a way to survive. Always in fear of capture. If it wasn't the police who were after you, it was your wife: Why don't you go out and get a job? Oh, I suppose there ain't any work that's *good enough* for you? Things that prep school kids would not understand, had not been raised to understand, might not ever understand. Why were black men so concerned about being black men? Why did they insist on making things so difficult to explain, making civil rights the perpetual subject of discussion—Watts was forever on the lips of white boys, wanting to know what it was like. Is it really that bad? Have you ever seen anyone shot? Is there really police brutality? Have you ever been shot at?

They had never seen the lonely unlit streets of Watts. Had never been afraid at night, typing or reading, of the animal sounds. Look out the window and see the dog packs roaming the streets of the projects, knock over and then forage through garbage cans, no one chasing them away but only watching. Green beast eyes glowing in the night, out of the night, and the moon, the moon's pale light, above your head as you gazed back into those eyes, into their unthinking depths, and heard the low guttural growls of the beast. He feared dogs, a feeling quite unlike even his closest friends on that campus, in that world. Negroes from middle-class backgrounds who had attended prep schools and achieved glowing records. Negroes from South Side Chicago housing projects who taught him how to light matches against the wind. Harvard Negroes, who believed in themselves and looked on life, all of life, as part of the game. The Education Game: to play it you have to seem it, have to become so much a part of the accepted stereotyped portraiture of the aspiring Negro that you finally become accepted. But acceptance was not really this feeling. It would have been as easy to accept the dog packs. Thoughts of Harvard, of the long-haired, well-groomed dogs that strode, romped through the Freshman Yard — friendly dogs, *cared for* by their owners. Could it be that in the dog packs, in Watts, he saw himself and his friends? So close to fighting over garbage, the garbage that life dumped out to you, in trash cans called haunted schoolyards and wind-swept playgrounds: where the only sound was the continual grating of the rings, the iron rings, suspended by chains, swinging back and forth over the sandpit, the housing projects silhouetted in the gray stormy weather against the horizon — one's face turned toward the projects above the buildings into the grayness of God's Heaven. Where little kids fought over games, spilled blood, and ran in gangs while inside those buildings, locked away from sight of the world, fought the owners of the children: to have the love of a child.

But what did they say whenever faced with this Hoodlum? Of course, thoughts arose concerning his maturity: what is a man that he tells of youth and youth's own fears, of dogs and people and the hardships, the tragedies. Not as if he were singing a song, but because he simply believed that he had lived this way and that in this survival, he had a particular influence which had to be realized sooner or later. There was fear of a growing rift in that Cambridge. Because he feared the eyes of man, the Hoodlum withdrew, regardless of their interest in his story. Tragedy had withdrawn as it only knew how: the universal had been tapped, no matter how slightly or unseemingly, in the lives of all who had grown to know him, and within that human shell another life was being born: I stepped forth, aware that a man can create a ghetto within the confines of his own mind. Stake out the preposed borderlines of blackness and whiteness: move at that instant into the outside world, itself both black and white, a world of externals and appearances: become two people, black and white, not Good and Evil. Learn to immerse oneself into the plights, the stories, of other people because you can tap the extent of sorrow in the lives of all you meet. Tell Negroes to beware of their blackness: it may be but another white man's values. Tell whites of how books, of how *Bleak House,* can become real, the fog a part of your nostrils: your sister pregnant and your mind totally detached from this reality: that you moved intermittently between Harvard and Watts, afraid of committing yourself to one or the other completely. No one could tell me anything. I knew what the answers were. There was only one question that had everyone confused.

It was the middle of the school year. It was the beginning of spring. Christmas was over and so, too, was much of the light-hearted air that had atmospherized Harvard Yard during its opening three months. Now, education had set in and our Hoodlum raised himself from his bed to look out of the window, to take stock of that change in the air, and then, to walk out of the door into the crisp thirty-degree weather before quickly retiring to his room. Damn, it's colder than hell out there! he would mutter — though, of course, the winter had been much colder. He was simply looking for an excuse not to go to class and this coldness was the best excuse he could find. Of course, it would soon be warm, but that did not matter. His bookshelf would always be there, big and with each day's trip to the Harvard Bookstore growing bigger (though we must remember that these book-buying excursions took place in the late afternoon when it had grown commensurately warmer). There was no thought in his mind of attending classes. Was he an ingrate, or a rebel, or a reactionary, some radical, perhaps, if it might not be asking too much, could he well have been simply involved in finding out what life was all about, or is that too simple? If he was a product of the slums, then of what slums, and what sort of product was he?

Did his eyes see Harvard: the Yard and the Yale Game behind, the counseling sessions over with, his position in the movement of things firmly established? No, not really that kind of world. It was too artificial, too involved with the processes of trying to make a better living when all he wanted was to simply let time pass by. He didn't know who Norman Mailer was, though *The Naked and the Dead* was out. Nor had he read James Joyce. *Finnegans Wake:* what was that? Or if one knew who Samuel Beckett and the race-screaming LeRoi Jones (who could sink down into the limpid surfaces of reality and come out with some pretty valid insights into the nature of homosexuality, which scares most college kids) were — then it was just as easy to assume a literary superiority, a greater racial awareness. He was not that involved, in other words, with the world situation at large. You had on your hands a kid who was genuinely wrapped up in trying to make meaning out of a wrecked life instead of scrapping all remembrances of it completely, then having the courage to admit this rejection consciously to himself, and then moving on to restructure a new world. Nothing unusual at all.

To then be aware of what life exacts of you, if one is concerned with this whole business of dying, and it was not the easiest task in the world for the Hoodlum. Many times he found himself using a borrowed joke from a friend to express his morning breakfast greetings in the old freshman dining quarters: "It's your world, squirrel. I'm just trying to get a nut!" And he was, he was in search of an orgasm of physical and spiritual revelation that could not be his consciously during that year because he had not opened himself up to the possibility of there existing other worlds of existence than his own. The typical white rebels were met, these rich kids who had turned away from their parents and those Cadillacs, black (as opposed to the loud whiteness, the white-on-white-in-white Cadillacs of Watts and any other Negro ghetto in America) which used to turn into the Yard on weekends, parents bringing candy and cookies and other various foodstuffs which sooner or later were eaten by everybody but the parents' kid. Like most poor kids, our man would see these goodies and say nothing. "You'll get tremendous cultural exposure!" one former Jordan teacher had told him before he left for Harvard. He did. In sarcastic, biting ways that might have been seen by others but was felt, registered internally, and then left there to realize itself days, weeks, hours, months, years later: perhaps as a sudden laugh, perhaps as a bitter cursing, perhaps a shame, perhaps, and then in greater proportions, as a concern with the twin shingles of the social measuring-scales upon which poverty and affluence are doled out: some suffer, some die, all of us learn what it is to want more. Another teacher had said, "Do you know what *enough* is? — just a little bit more!"

He was on academic probation — make up your grades or flunk out. Only nine out of that class of twelve hundred flunked out. A lot of others took leaves of absence to study themselves, and there were the perpetual Radcliffe cases: those unnamed medical leaves of absence so that some girl could have her illegitimate baby in peace. A world that was, in retrospect, quite similar to Watts. And yet, because of its tremendous freedom, there were the canoe rides on the Concord River where cold was the name of the air and pretty was the color of the fish, a great deal more warming. Most of the time life back home was cold. Parents here were people you could see and appreciate. Made you wonder why white kids would rebel. If you had the chance, you surely wouldn't walk out on a million-dollar inheritance.

The shocking realization was that this was me, JOHNIE, who had grown up in Watts and had seen policemen literally crack skulls open while women fell to their knees crying like babies at seeing their babies carried off to jail, who had seen his father's house burn to the ground, who had almost become inured to death and blood and tears. Too much of it spoils the novelty. My own morality was not based on a Western system of good and evil, traceable to Plato and Hesiod, Jesus and St. Augustine. Rather, it was a social and cultural orientation to the slums — in which evil was taken for granted and upon it erected a value system of happiness and terror. I knew that I was not alone. My friends, all of us who have been nursed on this world, live according to this system of values. This was something neither Chris Wadsworth, nor Dr. Cotton, nor anyone else in that entire place would have gathered, no farther than seeing a bit of the sun just before it sinks into the sea, and then, until the next day, is lost. They only saw the moon, good people for all that they were, showing human characteristics of love and warmth and sincerity in their work that make definite impressions but which could not at that time be extended into this many-surfaced world.

Some might run the risk of calling it all a dreamworld and they would be wrong, as wrong as those who would call the Hoodlum a racist when all he was, in truth, was a bearer of the imprint from that world. He was beyond even looking back upon his world and calling it sordid, brutal, with a frankness that at times had left him overwhelmed, typical advertising adjectives of revealing books. No, this for him was a dynamism that time and again cost him, cost him friendships and relationships that might have offered a way out of this reality into another: an escape. And he would have been glad for a hand toward escape, though now, when Harvard is superimposed over Watts, though the Hoodlum is placed above my own reflection in the mirror, I suppose there truthfully could have been no escape. Harvard had become a ghostyard, empty. There were animal sounds in the air. The snow had become brown and slushy. Snow was not pretty, it acted as an obstruction. In his way of travel, in my way, and everyone else's. People were laughing and looking real because they tasted joy denied to me. A man can flunk out of school for many reasons.

A man looking into himself must not look too hard, or the reflection will be encased within Reality's mirror. I saw mine, the entire story called the coming of the Hoodlum. I began to wonder if I might ever escape, so that I would come closer to my own salvation. That is right, for I had become a spiritualist, not a mystic. I had entered Harvard an atheist, who went home Christmas and sat in his mother's church taking notes on the Reverend's sermon and then, at the end of the services, when everyone went up and congratulated the minister on his ministerings, had shown where his dialectics differed considerably from his own exhortations to the good and plenty of the land.

On June 7, 1965, exactly nine months later, I returned to Watts. This time it was for keeps, if anything in life can be applied that label. But the Hoodlum was fired, fire: he believed in God. He had believed in the possibility of all men finally coming together, in truth, he had dedicated himself to some personal ministering of his own to the needs of his friends and companions, with whom he had shared the living experience, Watts. There, within that jet, the mind's eyes traveled both back and forth in time, seeing Harvard before arriving that September 21, 1964, and leaving that June day, seeing Christmas and seeing Jordan High, seeing all that he was. Most of all, understanding that things would have to be different from here on out. Something had happened, he did not know what. But there was one thing that had to be true: he was more than a year older, he had done a lot more than party late at night, or lose his virginity, or take Chinese Philosophy. He had changed. Back home.

The last thing he remembered reading in the Harvard *Crimson* was that applications this year for those 1,200 spots had risen to 6,500. To be sure, there would be more Negroes. It has been getting like that all across the country. But then, that was progress. This, 1965, would be the year, His year: his resolution. And in August of that year, Watts and all of Los Angeles would burn before he began understanding why life was so much dearer than death.

India

The bald-pate head bends back,
and the shadow of the horn
against the walls begins to
emit a sound sweet, clear, and
sad.

Death comes creeping in, large
and so frighteningly unafraid.
The sounds of the horn grow
and the shadow on the wall
glows.

Life is moving in behind death. And the
India of sad girls and hungry
boys begins to cry, the sobs
reaching my soul.

But then what are the blues but me
unable to help others. For so long
I have been myself, concerned with
my life and its passions. The cries
of others mean nothing.

And so it is with India. She moves across
continents crying bird's marrow while
rats bloody the streets of Harlem. It
is a sad tale, told with terror and
abandon.

India and her millions will starve slowly.
Harlem and its rats will die slowly.
Love and hatred will be born, they will
grow old, and then they will die.

Trees will bud,
the plants flower,
my life will become an end in itself.
And the blues will be the ballad named "India."

The Suicide Note

(ACCEPT, DO NOT QUESTION FACT: I HAD JUST CALLED MY MOTHER AND TOLD HER, BEYOND ALL THINGS ELSE, THAT I HAD ALMOST KILLED MYSELF. I CRIED AND NOW I WRITE THESE WORDS AND I FEEL EMPTY. THE WORDS COME FROM WITHIN ME, PAST BULLSHIT.)

If I was going to kill myself,
how would my mind wander? Or would
it dally, toying with the thought
of murder (like psychiatrists think
to themselves, "He'll do nothing now
because he's talking it over with
himself —
the moment of crisis is past.")

But then, when one considers suicide,
all else becomes totally irrational.
Life, even if it has been shitty,
means nothing. You strip everything
bare. And now I think that the purest
person in the world (because I have
studied him personally)
must have been Christ!

I would commit suicide in its purest
form — becoming the abhorred object of
all humanity, even my closest friends
(Budd, Harry Dolan, John Steacy,
Stanley Crouch, Watts, South LA).

I would not kill myself
with a gun,
or by drinking myself to death,
or with a knife,
or playing Richard Whitman
(except that I would have to use
Stanford's Hoover Tower

rather than that of the U. of Texas)
laying in a bird's nest
sniping off people
I'd never seen before
in my life.

I would go crazy,
becoming a babbling snot-nosed
idiot where all my I.Q. Tests
have shown me to be intelligent,
when being accepted into Harvard,
into Stanford,
(even, in fact, because it was hard
because I applied late)
into East Los Angeles Junior College.

I would not talk about
depressing things because
people have always read
my poetry (or heard me
read it to them)
and *complained* about the
depressing nature of the work.

I would not talk about
happy things because people
who knew me in my greatest moments
of personal weakness discovered
that I could cry,
not talking about being black
not talking about hurting people,
but about how
there are certain things that a person
is just not supposed to bear by himself.

Should I look at the world and say,
"Do not go gentle into that good night"?
Or should I go on and say what I feel,
that
you become a man when you

cry in front of your mother
and your friends —
exploding all the lies you ever
put out about your virility,
sexuality, ability to cope, not
merely with yourself but with
the bullshit put out by Norman Mailer
on the White Negro where he says
that the American Negro is rootless,
existentialist, alone,
the one true psychopath,

and that "hip"
is not smoking
marijuana.

You become a man when
you stop all of those faces
from coming out of your
mouth and begin shaping your
lips to sing the recognizable
features of your own past,

and what you know is true.

Hush

from LOVE, HUBBY'S GONE

"My Beloved!"
"Hush, the birds can hear!"
"What of flowers?
Or God's own children?
Nothing matters but the skies!"
"Hush, the birds can hear!"

But the flowers drip children
of flint, stones falling from the

birth-bed while the hollowed
  surgeons gasp and die, and mother
cries, seeing the monster
  spawned of human limb.
    "Baby, I've always wanted to have a son!"
    "We'll have one, honey!"

Behold
  the murdered child of Job
  laughs callously on the
  bed of birth,
    his mother crying because
    of the known,
      the coming terror.

Too many babies are burned
each year not to fumigate the stars,
too many babies have burned
their fathers' hearts not to rot the skies.
Still
  countless *babies* turn down stereo record-players
  and sink back into posh sofas,
  the reclining music casting a brief shadow:
  ladies' legs and girdles flying,
  babies born and people crying.

The music sounds good
    "I'm so dependent
    When I need comfort
    I always come running to you."
"Hush, the birds can hear!"

Bad News

No check
  in mailbox.
no food
  filling icebox.

No pity
  for sad.
no news
  called funny.

No tears
  dot the scar.
no nice
  to be happy.

No twists
  in life's play.
no frolic
  in the falling.

Just hands
  reaching out.
just a radio,
  through the window.

Shattered, glass
  (slivers of the spirit)
shattered, hands
  (longing to be loved)
shattered, bones
  (welcome to the bloodknot)

A feeling
  racing through the mind.
an impulse
  quickening the dead.

A house aflame,
  a mood forever lost.

Attention

Because it was never there,
 something empty filled the gap;
and since the absence was not seen,
 all too soon the people died.

They died as babies die
 who never knew mother love;
they died of want,
 they died crying for attention.

And though life's cycle yet goes on,
 with babies wailing life
 and mourners wailing death;
there yet existed that absence.

And the unmarked graves are empty,
as empty as the town that lies buried within them.

We cry for opportunity,
 for freedom now!
We scream for respect,
 human rights, and yet, once gained
 we still hold a rebellious enmity:

There is no feeling in this world,
 there was not ever . . . never noticed.

The Fish Party

The fish are gathering again tonight,
my dear.
Do you think we ought to watch them
(sit in for a few moments and tinker with our trumpets)
for a little while yet?

They're such darling creatures,
so small and vicious.

Do you think we ought to watch them
(sit in for a few moments with our trumpets of woe!)
for a little while yet?

I wonder what they'll be doing tonight?
The *big* one Goldie ate Russ last night.
Do you think we ought to watch Goldie
(how many young boys die across the seas?)
for a bit tonight?

Cannibal hunters from the deeper consciousness —
the small fish —
are killer whales coursing the mental current,
devouring all vestiges of conscience and morality.
The only survivors,
now floating a raft down the ocean of the ego,
are a couple of thin creatures named
Sorrow and Tomorrow.

John! O John! The fish are gathering tonight.
It looks like they're having a party.
Don't you think we ought to watch
(how many insensitive super-patriots
sneeze when the cat-tails of the public
indignation comes forth, flaying the
raw hides of conservatives and radicals?)
for just a little while? Huh?

Hey, look? Goldie has just eaten Jesus up!

Jeremy

I am Jeremy's bearer.
I walk gladly through jungle grass,
bearing Jeremy's burden.
I sing gladly to the leopard,
to the jackal, of Jeremy's burden.
I am Jeremy's bearer.

My black legs are churning
through the river's heart
(and I pray to the river-god:
do forgive this, my sacrilege.
I do this only for Jeremy).
I am a black bearer.

My machete is cutting
the vines away,
so that we may pass.
My men are marching,
yes, chanting to the lion:
"Black Bwana dead . . . Black Bwana dead."

I am Jeremy's bearer.
I walk gladly through jungle grass,
bearing the burden of Jeremy.
I sing gladly to the leopard,
to the jackal, of Jeremy.
"Black Bwana dead . . . Black Bwana dead."

Intent

If, in the beginning,
there was love
(and love moved as
a man stepping from
stone to stone to
finally cross the river)

If, in the beginning,
there was a clear eye
(and thought formed
as if man were moving
from star to star,
and finally to destiny)

If, in the beginning,
there was purpose

(and silence grew
as though plants were
flourishing in some
proverbial garden)

Then why, as we live,
do we hate and not love
(while rivers grew
to swollen proportions
and logjams built
mounds of filth)

Then why, as we live,
does the unwanted child cry
(above dark hills
hang suspended blue
stars and a child asks,
Why does a slum have stars?)

Then why, as we live,
is there chaos within sanity
(silence
has always been
a deafening sound;
it is a peace that frightens)

If there was Intent, and it was good,
though good is blinded and men staggered on;
If there was meaning, and this had a value,
though feelings are blotted and cares fly away;
If there was happiness, and this brought tears,
though the people cry out, shame and sorrow reign;
If there was Intent, and it was good,
then why this emptiness and blue stars,
like so many hanging lanterns, above a slum?

Chaos in a Ghetto Alley

I am a little girl playing in my yard.
My mother is calling me into the house.

I am a little boy who is walking through the projects.
My mind is calling me into incinerators to make love.

We are the two who are one
we are male and female
whose genitals match perfectly
and whose fruits are ugly statistics.

I am the son of the other man
whose face was not blurred in the water,
whose mind was not lost in the mirror,
whose soul was not lost in the fires of August.

We are the sons of hate
We are the daughters of love
whose mothers have always called us,
whose desires have always called us,
whose need for father has always called us.

We were never children of the sun
who might bask beneath golden rays and burn red.
We were never children of darkness
whose mists shroud the stealing of thieves
or a whore-slaying Jack the Ripper.

Why do we lose the sounds out of our throats
and remember aimless dogs whose only needs
are for offspring and phone poles and fire hydrants?

We are night and today creatures
breathing in yesterday
whose minds have left today
to die in the foul clutches of tomorrow.

We are yesterday people
who cannot live in tomorrow.
What must be done must be done by our children.
And they burn fires in the alleys.

Black Consciousness

A need
to blackness
hurts the brown
shadow
falling softly
on the leaves.

From the begging
of sufferers
come the
games that abort
our lives; and so,
our souls have
the need to cry,
to be at times
felt, and
so,
pitied.

Perhaps
pity slept beneath
the sand dune and
bought a taste,
a hunger which will not die
in milk cartons and traveling,
temporarily sated
by a lie.
Or the inconsistency
of the lie
sticks to marrow —
clings to teeth,

or yet,
will not be lost.

Who lies
rejects
it.

It
alone
conscious. A black man
aware and so to be feared.
A need
to blackness thrills
the old leaf falling
softly
to the ground.

Alan Paton Will Die

Hidden away, nestled
  in a corner of the sadness,
mourns a black bird.

Fire has come
  to the woods, and
of all the kings,
  only animals died.

Fire has come
  to the streets
of the *other* world,
  and only fire died.

Should the forests
  see a sun kissing
a beloved country,
  perhaps they would die.

Street covered
  by the darkness of

a shattered dream's wrath
    safe no more for walking.

Street burned over
    by the anger of a dying father
safe no more from the disbelieving son
    screaming a tear-glazed blindness.

Perhaps the world
    will solve itself
and be blown to pieces.

Perhaps the world
    will grow fearful,
listening to the lonely
    mourning of the *black* bird.

Long Live the Peace Corps of America

Long Live the Peace Corps of America!
May their deeds be remembered as long as they live!
And if Mary killed that precious lamb,
a fleece as white as snow
(no trick ending to come)
Then Mary herself was a sodomist
and a murderer.

America, eroica, erotica,
pot for the ages,
acid for the millions,
starvation for the underfed.

Nightmare, daydream, flowers budding
as old children give birth to
young women. People sprout and
infants rule while bombs blast
cities, havoc rises from the
blasted incinerators of riot-torn
animals.

Guilt greedily follows the pregnant scent
of machine-bitches, whose glinting
armor reeks of *My Sin* while wheat
is dumped in the Atlantic Ocean and
Joe Bell, All-American Black Boy, hangs
his head against a project-bush,
turning Canadian Club to his lips,
cursing the army of the president
while professional virgins hock their
bodies and a dozen people more walk
down the street, *benny*-stuffed penguins.

Eroica is a bitch.
I look at my fantasy and decide,
alongside psychiatrists,
that *my* neurosis is my environment.

Empty forms build strong houses of music —
dope addicts worship black drums,
young girls fuck in backrooms of
piss-stained stairways with the inimitable
style of old whores.

How much can a man grow in America? —
whose breath is sweet if one reads
billboards advertising the prosperity
of mortuaries (this is the US/A) . . .
if one drives American-made cars through
broken glass, crying babies, running
over the first, and away from the second.

Heaven is a garbage dump —
a big brick church with a preacher
(He was strong!) I decide for Christ:
but I *also* choose Bird, Lady Day,
and the million smackheads who dance across
my daydreams in school wearing marijuana leaves
for dresses.

I have returned to Africa.

Watts, 1966

Yes, the call was
    for violence
and it filled the
    air, it seemed,
    everywhere

No, nothing was gained
    that felt no fire
before the first trace
    of sun broke over
    the morning dawn.

It was a ship only fools
    chose to ride, and the
hopes of those angry black
    braves crowded the skies
    and the seas and the land.

For Watts, amid all the
    shouting and cursing
and foot stamping and
    screaming, the sight
    of routed white colonialists

was heady wine. Perhaps, when
    I sat to watch the images
weaving against the walls, I
    saw myself reflected in the
    wildness of their oaths and stares.

Oaths, that laid torch to a cross
    on this, the yard of my brain.
My mind burned with the ache
    to get away . . . escape the
    bestricken, howling rabble.

I wanted a place to sit and
    there ponder . . . a spot away

from them and the black women
  who shouted "Rape" and the
  old men slobbering their words

and said stories with their
  magnificently wine-twisted mouths.
I had thought to sink into
  a daydream, singing a quiet
  song to and with myself.

. . . to look across the streets
  torn by the rioting and now
mocked by an apathetic white merchantry
  and wonder if the hate within
  my soul would ever leave.

Oh . . . bright, young guns poured,
  spilled out into the streets
to raise a din of noise that echoed
  from Central Avenue to Alameda
  to Imperial Highway to Manchester Avenue.

A din of sound that called people,
  who rose, it seemed, from the
very manholes that gutted the streets
  . . . streets, a patchwork quilt
  of incensed cesspools civilized

Man has named "ghettoes."
  But still, the fervor of revolution
inflamed the air. Air,
  draped as though a pregnant cloud
  above the tiny heads of black children

playing in the streets with their lives.
  A fire hydrant, overturned and now
spewing water as if it were a whale in
  the midst of miscarriage 50 feet high
  while buses honked impatiently

and the hustler's hawklike stare commanded
  a visitor's noting.
Pity, Sorrow, Love, each fought
  silent savage battles throughout
  the night for the lost souls

that wandered drunkenly in the alleys
  or sat, composed, on milk crates
in front of the liquor stores —
  speaking of filth and Mighty Whitey
  and the bloodlust that has impregnated

even the little bastard child sitting
  on a porch, confused by the chaos.
BROFOYEDUR: the white man has indeed
  created a nightmare, and that Hell
  will not have Watts surprises none

but the mayor. On, on come the all-seeing
  eyes of the television cameras
controlled by the probing, insensitive
  hand of the detached reporter who
  purports to relate the news to millions

while there, in the eye of madness,
  he quakes in his boots and wonders
when his turn to be beaten shall come.
  (Left bleeding like a brutalized ragdoll
  that has outlived its usefulness and

a child's curiosity.) Relating the news
  while the reality perpetuates itself.
Strutting down the streets
  come the Young Ones,
with jazz playing from FM radios
  and marijuana tucked away
  in a jacket,

talking 'bout the Man and
  the trial of Deadwyler

and the coming of the end
 of the fire that burned
 too short too long ago

and yet something new,
 a man named Fear,
to the world as it looked
 in palsied horror at
 this, the child of the
 Hydrogen Bomb.

Watts, a womb from whence
 has been spawned molotov
cocktails and shotguns, but most
 of all, a lack of care:
 for care has been exposed

as fraudulent and so deserving
 of no due other than that
accorded burnt newspaper wafting
 away in blackened wisps while
 mothers hang out their clothes

and talk on telephones of the
 danger and their children
and the nightmare that has descended
 . . . and how hopelessness,
 helplessnessness, is their

young one's due.
 The man named Fear has inherited half an acre,
 and is angry.

VALLEJO RYAN KENNEDY, born in

December, 1947, in Boston, Massachusetts, moved to Texas at an early age, then to California in 1957. In high school, in Watts, he took science as his major subject, but his main interests were art and writing. Shortly after graduation he moved in with his school chum, Leumas Sirrah. He also met Ernest Mayhand, and "our sister Sandra." These three young men have all been members of the Workshop since early 1966 and, with Sandra, they face the world with *Umajo* ("togetherness") as their motto. Vallejo Ryan Kennedy has taken the pen name *Sanamu* from a Swahili word meaning "work of art in the form of a statue." He has also written special material for a musical group that calls itself "Because We're Black." He is a resident of Douglass House and serves on its Writers' Council.

Another Day

Another day without a dollar
another dog without a collar
another day of strain and hell
another day in Whitey's cell.

Again the 'psych' by bulls, for fear
again the thought of leaving here
again the yell it's time to hop
again we go eat Whitey's slop.

Returning from a so-called meal
with stomach that it didn't fill
eating Hershey bar or two
with hope of it doing what chow didn't do.

I hear of home and other places
I see the look of hate on faces
I hear the call of "grab a hole"
I see my cell door bang and close.

Receiving treatment due a slave
told when to shit and shower and shave
receiving orders on intercom
told 24 hours dusk and dawn.

They're opening A-Row, new fish arrived
watch that gate, fish, get inside
they're breaking 'em down now, it's store time
so watch that gate and get in line.

Grab your towel — shower route
A-Row clear? Everyone out?
It's dayroom time anybody goes
Is A-Row clear? They're coming close.

Then you're back to your cell again
your cell door opens you step back in
late at night when it's time to sleep
your mind again vividly repeats:

Another day without a dollar
another dog without a collar
another day of strain and hell
another day in the county jail.

Love of a Woman

Love of a woman, the peace
of a man
love of a woman, the worry
of a man
love of a woman, the life
of a man
love of a woman, the death
of a man

Love for a woman, the strength
of a man
love for a woman, the weakness
of a man
love for a woman, the good
of a man
love for a woman, the bad
of a man

Love in a woman, the making
of a man
love in a woman, destruction
of a man
love in a woman, success
of a man
love in a woman, the failure
of a man

Love and a woman, the joy
of a man
love and a woman, the sorrow
of a man
love and a woman, the heaven

of a man
love and a woman, the hell
of a man

My Black Man's Togetherness Was Called Revolt

What I heard was heaven to hear
What I felt was heaven to feel
What I saw was hell to see
What I knew took hell to find

When it was heard my ears were glad
When it was felt my soul was proud
When it was seen my thirst cried for blood
When it was known my life I offered

Where it was heard was the suddenly opened ears of the world
Where it was felt was the heart of the black man
Where it was seen was a place I called home
Where it was known was in the history of the world

Those who heard it were appalled to hear
Those who felt it were the black grief-stricken mothers
Filling the black graves of their sons dug by the white man
Those who saw it were young and old staring at the face of death.
Those who knew it were the 33 fallen blacks.
Togetherness was called revolt.

ERNEST A. MAYHAND, Jr.

says, "My father, whose stage name was 'Skillet,' was a vaudeville performer of some note." By 1946 the number of jobs for people in that profession had sharply declined, and "for our family of eleven, already living without luxury, the birth of twins (my brother and me) that year came as a shock." Ernest Mayhand was born and brought up in Los Angeles. When he reached the age of thirteen, he tried to help by moving out on his own, and says that he lived by his wits "as much like a tomcat as a teen-ager." He dropped out of school before graduation. In 1966 he became Coordinator of the Student Council of the Youth Training and Employment program at the Westminster Neighborhood Association. It was then that he met Leumas Sirrah and Vallejo Kennedy, who introduced him to the Watts Writers' Workshop. He has since begun to evolve a new identity, and has joined with other friends to form an organization called "Youth Organization for Progress," which is designed to deal directly with community problems. He also envisions himself as a poet, and adds, "perhaps there is a little vaudeville in me." He is a resident of Douglass House, where he is employed as custodian and also serves on the Writers' Council.

Life, a Gamble

What is not a gamble?
A wise man's thought
a gamble.
Merely to exist
a gamble.
To believe in yourself
a gamble.
He she or it
a gamble.
To walk on a street
to stand and wait
to love and hate
a gamble.
To live in past
think in future
be at present
all a gamble.

Then why gamble to excess —
shuffle cards, shake dice?
A man gambles with love
gambles working his saw.
But gambling with his *green*
is anger gambling
murder gambling —
Your life's the stake!

JAMES THOMAS JACKSON

JAMES THOMAS JACKSON hitch-hiked to Watts, Los Angeles, from his hometown, Houston, Texas, arriving there the last night of the August riots. Though an avid reader from his "mother's knee onward" (he is forty years old), he was a dropout from high school when he entered the Army; but he continued to read, and took more than fifteen correspondence courses while he was in the Army. Mr. Jackson joined the Watts Writers' Workshop in its "Coffee House" period, in the spring of 1966. His was one of the "Angry Voices of Watts" on the celebrated NBC-TV show of August, 1966, commemorating the revolt of the year before. Since joining the group he has sold two pieces to *West,* the Sunday Magazine of *The Los Angeles Times.* He helped build Douglass House with his own hands, and now serves as its press officer. "Shade of Darkness" is part of a novel-in-progress with the same title.

Reveille

HE WAS RUNNING TO BEAT THE BAND.

Reveille was four minutes to the front of him and his legs were churning like smoothly oiled pistons down that long, narrowly winding, foreign road. He *had* to make it, what with those brand-new corporal stripes so dearly sweated for and so newly gained; and the first overnight pass he'd acquired after five months of becoming part of this proud and wonderful outfit. That and his first experience of living in a remarkably strange land.

The Quartermaster insignia on his left shoulder arm gleamed brightly as he ran. The bright haze of a breaking summer dawn in his view revealed the stark outline of one-storied, wooden billets in the swiftly approaching distance. He ran tirelessly, like the well-conditioned athlete he was. He saw Francis Scott Key being run up the mast — and put on more power. Thank goodness, he thought, the flag detail *always* beat morning roll call. Still, though, he couldn't take any chances. He'd have to hurry. . . .

His feet were gobbling up the narrow road. The outline of a barbed-wire fence encircling the camp's perimeter came clearer to his view. Even from this distance it looked like a shabby piece of goods for an American military installation. His face darkened at the sight of it. It always did. It looked like the ugly, fucking shanties that he came from. His eyes swept over this old, unsightly, former DP *Lager,* with about eight huts in all, now the military haven encompassing *his* Quartermaster Company. Even the grass didn't grow anymore. Externally, their wooden surfaces had been painted so much — by dissident painters, no less — that their rotten sidings and flopping facades rebelled at each new approach of paint buckets in unskilled or uncaring hands. He grimaced at the thought but kept on running.

To top it off, as he grew closer, he saw the kraut civilian guards in their black-dyed, "fuzzy-wuzzy" uniforms and white helmets with black stripes running down the middle. Armed with carbines, no less!

Wasn't white folks crazy? What were the sons of bitches *there* for? To keep unwitting interlopers out? Or, to keep *his* Company *in?* Wasn't that a bitch!

They didn't control the main gate, though. The "brothers" had that. He was *really* glad of that. Even though he was sure to make it in there with just the barest amount of time, he would be recognized instantly as another "brother," and that would be that. When they had the krauts on at the beginning they were always checking passes. They were sticklers at it. *"Kenkarte, bitte, Kenkarte, bitte";* goddam, he sure was glad that was out. Damn! They sure could make it tough for the po' GI. He ran on, shaking his head.

He ran slower now, observant in the day's perspective, seeing the first few fatigue-clad stragglers drag sluggish bones into the narrow asphalt street between the huts. A smile lighted up his face: no need for further haste now; all was well, and he was home.

After all, that's what this was to him now: home. (He couldn't say this out loud, of course; people would think he wasn't used to anything.) Sure, this was an all-colored outfit — but a good one, and he was proud to death of it. Lately he had been hearing more and more talk that the colored and white soldiers were going to merge together, and he wasn't sure whether he would like that or not. (What the hell: he couldn't stop it one way or the other.) Just as long as they didn't do it too soon. When a man comes from nothing, like he did, and at his present age — twenty-five, right on the button! — gets worked into something, like an ace driver-mechanic in this famous Quartermaster Company, it was something to run, jump, and shout about.

He was looking between the buildings as he ran with that graceful stride that runners make when they are far ahead of the opposition, seeing more members of his unit pouring out of the huts toward the formation point. He ran driftingly now — "cooling it," gathering together his thoughts of last night's meanderings, to be discussed over the breakfast chow table with his buddy. He wouldn't have much to say this time. After all, he hadn't "scored" — as so many of the others had. Strangely, he had wanted those corporal chevrons worse than anything. The world was full of chicks, but those stripes were *hard* to come by. That first three-year hitch for instance: always waiting and working up to that instant, and then missing out right at the door. Now he had walked in — and had been accepted.

Oh, he had made a pass at a cute little filly at a coffee house in the city during the early part of the evening. But that was because he felt he had to do something to keep the broad from staring so intently at his dark face. Being black was such an exasperating thing over here. They stared at you from sunup to sun-aint, especially them country hicks from behind the mountains. They were gapers from the *be*-gin. So, while he was "cooling it" in this *real* nice coffee house, drinking Napoleon brandy by the double shot and chasing it with beer, he had "hit" on the broad just to see if she was interested in him or merely gaping at his dark face.

He didn't get anywhere and she turned her head away from him so sharply he thought she'd break her neck. After a time he forgot all about her, and drank toasts to his promotion in silence. He walked awhile, enjoying the summer night, thinking over a home he had never loved and had *always* wanted to get away from. He walked the hinterland route because it was good for night thinking, and quieter; the stars, far in their heavens, hung more peacefully. Inwardly he had felt that the man of momentum which he was striving to be had finally gained some. Now he could go along in the life he had made up his mind to live: that of a career soldier. So if he was asked how he celebrated his promotion and his overnight pass, these would quite likely be the things he would tell them — although in a different way, of course. He slowed down almost to a halt as he entered the guard gate, flanked by a white, circular edifice that divided entrance and exit. A khaki-clad Negro soldier with an MP brassard on his arm and a forty-five on his hip stepped out of the small house at the gate's center. He nodded affirmatively as he recognized the runner's face, and with his thumb beckoned him on in.

Walking now, he strutted monkeylike to the nearly formed formation. He adopted this clownish act only because a friend's face greeted him a scant few smiles away. (It's easy to be friendly with naturally effusive friends.) He felt joyful. After all, his expression seemed to say, didn't he spend the whole night away from camp and just barely make it for The Man's reveille? (Every swinging root in the *Lager* knew that that Georgia Cracker of a Company Commander was a bitch with his reveille. *No*body, *no* time, *no* time missed that diffy-daffy motherfucker's reveille. Shit, not even MacArthur, hell!) Dog-gone right. But he couldn't tell his friend that he had bought a jug of cognac and carried it with him on his nocturnal travels — alone, got good and drunk, and a little sick, and had to spent the night in a roadside *gasthaus* till morning came. You just could not tell your best buddy these things. They sounded too incredible. People in his age group expected victories, not defeats. So he'd have to white lie a li'l bit.

"Lookit the kid!" Evident proudness, showing in his friend's voice.

"Aw, it ain't no happen's." Nonchalance showing through and through.

"Don't give me that shit. I know you done 'em up. Had yo'self a young ball!"

More nonchalance. Silent braggadocio, emphasized by shaking one stiffly outstretched hand from side to side as though the thing were of no moment. "I ain' raisin' no sand. The nest is wa'am, but the bird is gone." Contemptuously immodest, provoking laughter, completely understood, without long-winded embellishments — they will come later and the lies will flow with each encouragement — this unerudite by-play must be carried on in the brief time remaining.

"Let's have that noise! COMPANY, TEN HUT!" Repartee ends. The roaring voice of one thoroughly disciplined first sergeant brings with one command one blatant sound of eighty-six pairs of feet present for duty. In itself it is enough. The owners of those eighty-six pairs of feet present for duty out of a company of 125 total strength have heard that voice through innumerable tones, inflections, and decibels. But on this bright summer morning there is an urgency in it totally unlike all those other times before. The hush in its wake grows apprehensively maddening. The affirmation that something is wrong comes in the next, hardly ever used command.

"OPEN RANKS, MAARCH!"

Obediently the first line on the front rank takes three steps forward and halts. The third line in back takes two backward steps. The middle line stands fast. One or two overtly inquisitive heads furtively try to ask one another the inevitable questions of Why or What. They as well as all the others are petrified into immobility by an amazingly clever command:

"FREEZE!"

The now frozen human statues are stock-still. Every eye looks straight ahead, an ocean of wonderment on those immobile faces. A door from the Orderly Room just in front of them opens and the Company Commander — a white man, The Man — precedes a white provost marshal followed by a young golden-haired, white woman.

The look on the Company Commander's face is stern, deliberate, even angry. The Provost Marshal's face is intent, authoritative. The young girl's face is milk-white and she looks as though she is scared to death! At the formation the Captain addresses the First Sergeant, who stands stiffly implacable at attention, then does an impressive about-face, walks to the head of the first man in the column, and becomes the first man in the column, frozen as his predecessor.

Now the Captain takes the lead, starting with the First Sergeant. The girl is in the center, the Provost Marshal is behind. They walk slowly, deliberately so, past each man, all the way down the line of the first rank. The life blood of each black or colored man within these three lines is now in the hands of this undeniably beautiful, young, white woman, irrespective of their presence in another country. True, their faces do not move, nor their bodies; it is only the souls peering through those brown eyes that have a tendency to give vent to their true feelings. And those souls cannot speak now. Indeed, they do not dare!

The trio turns, looks up and down the backs and necks of each man in that column; and *that* is worse because they cannot see behind their heads! Not another word has been spoken, nor does one need to be uttered. Every man-jack in that formation knows that some overzealous paramour-to-be has attempted an assault upon this white feminine symbol of the world. They know that this type of crime — and worse — happens and has happened in other armies of the world. But never — NEVER! in the souls of black folk — does it happen exactly like this. Suddenly, the trio turns again at the first man in the second line and begins that long, slow, deliberate walk again. The drama intensifies.

Seven men down is the Runner. He recognizes the girl as the same one that he barely spoke to last night. He stiffens suddenly and the Captain sees the motion. Six men down. Five. *Shee-it! S'pose this bitch stops at me! Hell, ain't no law 'gainst hittin' on a woman. Goddam.* But if for just some feminine whim she stopped at him, then what? How could he explain where he was? He hadn't met a soul in his travels. He was in and out of joints, trying to find one that suited his mood. *Oh, God, make this bitch pass on by!* Three. *But she looked at me for such a helluva long time.* Two. Arrogance, the only course left, seeping subtly into his clouded stream of consciousness. *Bet they put the bitch up to it.* One. Anguish. Defeat. *Oh, Jesus, what am I gonna do!*

Zero.

She did not pass on. She just stood there and smiled him the warmest smile, as though he were an old friend she hadn't seen in ages!

The Captain's face held a satisfied leer. The Provost Marshal's hand went automatically to his gun holster — and stayed there. They both looked so smug, so self-contained, that in his sudden flight he pushed them aside so brusquely he had a head start before they could even recover. (They didn't know it, but the "Brothers" gave him a few precious seconds with fumbling apologies and idiotic interferences.) By that time he was a damned good distance away.

He was running to beat the band. Only this time he was not running like at the beginning, with a purpose, trying to make it in, looking athletic, concerned, and proud, with a zest for living, hope for tomorrow, *today!* Now he was running like a fool, legs akimbo, frightened running, ever listening for the bullet that was sure to come from the Provost Marshal's gun. All his *life* he had been running, Great God Almighty! For something. To something. Last night with the promotion and the overnight pass he felt he had stopped running. Because he had finally arrived at his destination, more or less. This morning he was running back to it, hoping to go on, with less hurried strides, "cooling it," so to speak. Now he was running for all he was worth, more into oblivion than anything. Home — for what it was worth — was over three thousand miles away. But he was a good runner. He'd make it.

He had to slow down for the fence. The civilian guard said something to him. In one instant he looked at him with such venom that one would think the look alone would freeze him into immobility. He didn't answer. He didn't need to. Wasn't going to. He was part-way over the fence when the sound from the carbine stopped him short. The guard was a marksman. The lone bullet went through his throat and his body draped arc-wise across the barbed wire, dangling ridiculously for several life-beats. Then all was still.

Only not quite all. Back at the disjointed formation was the throng of people headed toward him. The Runner's friend, his rotund frame quivering from his anguish at the scene unfolded, was walking just half a step behind the girl. The Captain and the Provost Marshal were just ahead of them. The Runner's friend was alternately looking at the fence in front of him and the girl to his left. Her conversation — to the void — was a tower of Babel as she walked among that varied group to where the body lay. But he heard the anguish being emitted in her mother tongue, recognized the words for their meaning. Suddenly he reached out and grabbed her hand and yelled to the two white forces of power in front of him:

"Wait, y'all, wait! Listen to her!" Pointing, holding on to her firmly. "It wasn' *him*. Ask her, ASK HER!"

They all stopped. The Captain and the Provost Marshal turned and walked back toward the woman, who was now lamenting to the heavens as the rotund body of the Runner's friend sank to the earth on his knees and alternately pointed at her and beat the ground with his fists. In all that silence his tears and sobs enveloped them in his anguish.

He lay there sobbing, beating the ground, saying those same words over and over: "Ask her, ask her, ask her," while every person there looked down sorrowfully at him.

Shade of Darkness

They were so drunk they didn't know who their adversaries were, where they had come from, or how they themselves had come to this particular pass.

Just a few minutes ago they were having a drunken ball in the place just down the street, even doing an impromptu jig or two on the dance floor to an incongruous and "square" accompaniment of zither music. It was late — darn near twelve, anyway — and icy cold outside, where the second snows had packed solid with their annual Christmas "visit." The cold itself hadn't bothered them — not with the many double shots of antifreeze they had poured into their gullets. The Three-Star Cognac they had been guzzling since sundown had provided a furnace to their glowing countenances as they stepped out the door, wishing both their much-relieved hosts and the other patrons a profusive barrage of *Fröhliche Wehnachtens* and Merry Christmases, respectively. (After all, soldiers were sometimes troublesome when there was so much drinking. And the *schwartzis* . . . sometimes they could be difficult . . .) For one instant, Paul felt a peculiar uneasiness when the door closed behind them. Like they were utterly alone.

By all that was holy and — to military men in particular — by all that was *conceivably* tactical, they should have taken the longer way home. But such old-maidenly fears seemed so commonplace tonight — of all nights. This was the Night of Noel, the "night of our dear Saviour's birth." This was O Holy Night and they were wrapped joyously up in it as they walked stumblingly, staggering happily, singing, down the cold, quiet, cobblestoned street. They were in love with everybody! Kendall blurted out suddenly: "Peace on earth! Good will to ever' body's body!"

There were at least four of them, maybe five. Paul only vaguely saw one of the assailants sneak furtively away after one of his intended blows was warded off and one of formidable power given in return — with a crunching sound against the jawbone. The impact of the blow greatly enlarged the eyes of the sneaky assailant-to-be, and the last Paul saw of him was a hasty departure. So there were six, at first.

One thing of which the two were certain: the thugs were all white. The evil glimpsed on their faces in such close combat was magnified manyfold in their rushing charges: swinging, kicking, cursing, some of it unmistakably Southern and *all* of it unmistakably vehement. They were attempting to do with sheer force of numbers — collective feet and knees and hands — that which white men in a dogged South had over the years done with rope and faggot to other black men just like them, with the same collective hatred. Only here there was one starkly immediate difference: the manner of dress, a uniform, was the same for *every* man involved in this upheaval. Now it was as though an Army was ridding itself of an Army. Its own. That unity of the form-fitting olive-drab symbol of American defense was never to be sacrosanct again; its causes were lies, its doctrines impeachable, its tenets spurious, and after one hundred and seventy-five years and more no American soldier ever again was to be his military brother's keeper. The dim light of a quarter moon, playing peek-a-boo with drifting, fleecy white clouds, reflected an incongruous scene of men at war — with themselves. It was unreal, unimaginable — to a passing stranger, perhaps — but to the two victims involved it was quite real, quite imaginable, only surprising that it had taken so long to reveal itself; they were the recipient pawns of one of America's smoldering hates.

They sought refuge in the wall together, almost simultaneously — Kendall leading the way, backing up to it, swinging, kicking, Paul following. They were in an area where both had walked, as it seemed to them, a thousand times: always for some normal reason, but, strangely, *always* in daylight. They knew it like the backs of their hands. A civilian cleaning and pressing shop fronted the end of this cul-de-sac. (The proprietor, a short, grubby-looking man, with a moustache like Groucho Marx, had a legion of young peasant women who scrubbed their clothes with the harsh GI soap, and water from a running stream in a small culvert to the left and rear of the building. They pressed them with hand irons that were constantly heating in a bucket of coals, just to the right of the door's entrance. The creases themselves hung alone! The owner should have made a mint, because he had trade from all the units in the area!) A shoe-repair shop with what Sergeant Moment described as having "qualitative extras" sat in the middle of the block. They bought their winter shoes there — and wore them all summer long: bought them handmade, had them repaired there, loved the rabbit fur that lined the insides. They were durable, long-lasting, had a classy look to them, and were thoroughly approved by Army protocol. Minnow's favorite commercial for them was: "Snow grip, can't slip," and he was right as rain. They purchased these shoes with money or trade: cigarettes, Nescafé, nylons from the Main PX, even with clothes from the duffel bags of their own Form Thirty-Two! There was also a restaurant that unostentatiously served a deluxe European cuisine at a surprisingly economical price; it looked, from the outside, like any simple *Weinstube* that doted on quality and comfortable sit-ins rather than on hullabaloos and grand-scale advertising. (The two warriors should know: they had just left the place.) Shops adorned either side of the short street. A two-storied *Konfektionär's* store flanked the opposite side of the cleaning shop. A hewn-out break in the continuous wall, which was made of stuccoed links, was the only aperture, and it gave onto a view of an open field, now thoroughly snow-covered. White soldiers used this opening as a ladder, hoisting themselves over it to reach their unit, some four blocks behind it. It was a direct shortcut. Verboten it was — but to a soldier, a shortcut. Otherwise, to the eyes of all concerned, the continuous wall, with its curving nooks and niches, completely sewed the street off in cemented finality. It was the wall alone that kept them from being whipped to pieces.

The moonlight was inconsistent. Nearly all the street lights from the restaurant on were dark. A faint bulb from the *Konfektionär's* shop glowed dully a scant hundred feet away. Darkness encompassed the battlers. The area was quiet, save for the sounds of blows being leveled or glanced off heads and resounding torsos and/or swishing misses in the air, aimed at a groin or thigh. The two were steadfastly pummeled by the five remaining assailants and swung back desperately in return. (Instantly the thought occurred to Paul: This is how the race riot in Italy started: a couple of spooks in the wrong place at the wrong time — and alone!) Paul had never before in all his life had a fight that mattered — except that fiasco with Rose and her boyfriend back in Boston. Yet five years of soldiering had taught him how. No one needed to tell him they were being attacked on the strength of hatred alone, on the strength of their being black, or on the strength of their association with white fräuleins in their midst. He knew. Reasoning did not hang in the balance here: he did; and Kendall did; and Race did. Every uniformed Negro from his battalion, and every Negro from other battalions, companies, squads, units, echelons and every Negro that was born this morning, yesterday, last night, the day before, ever after — every Negro everywhere on the face of this earth was being viciously clobbered by this desperately vicious quintet of white men whose violent passions of hatred had at last reached their peak — on them — and whose tumultuous hatred could only be satisfied by lying in wait for two unsuspecting blacks. And *because* Paul knew that reason was, in this case, especially *now,* just some pompous old bitch — printed, edited, and propagandized by a score of didactic, selfish, mendacious white men in the celestial seat of social power — he lashed back at the mean, angry, hateful faces with all the energy he could muster, using every dirty trick he could pull, avoiding kicks at his groin (which was obviously what they most despised, because that was damned sure the most repeated place they struck at), and returning kicks to their groins, guts, and heads whenever he saw an opening. Just think: a few minutes ago he was drunk as a Cooty Brown, happy as a lark, in a festive mood, singing Christmas carols at the top of his voice with Kendall, alternately reciting poems by James Whitcomb Riley and Paul Laurence Dunbar. Now he was mad as a motherfucker and this madness gave him additional strength.

Once he looked over at Kendall. The bright, clear, friendly eyes that he knew so well were now fixed in a pronounced stare of masochistic and sadistic welcoming. For every blow he received he retaliated with two. Sometimes he actually appeared to smile. To Paul it seemed as if this was Kendall's last day on earth, and the determined look on his friend's face revealed that he was going to take into his record book as many sore heads and bruised behinds as he could carry. His head was bleeding, and his mouth. He clamped his teeth hard, he winced often, he breathed laboriously, and the long, sinewy, strong arms were rapierlike in their powerfully directed agility. Hardly ever did he throw one that did not connect. Then they were wrestled, their assailants trying feverishly to get them away from the wall, to get them down on the ground, to stomp them into the dust. They would not yield (indeed, they did not dare!) nor fall, although by all odds existent they should have. They stood, however weakly, and swung and kicked and gouged, fighting for all the world like two invincible supermen.

Suddenly a noise appeared from nowhere — an automobile, the unmistakable sound of a jeep. Now, for one instant, all combatants stopped, their actions halted in ludicrous poses at confirmation of the sound. It arrested them all with its familiarity. Then, as a body, the assailants turned and ran, grabbing pete caps and straggling comrades in their wake, racing toward the opening in the wall. Paul distinctly heard their feet scraping the stucco as they climbed gasping over the wall, heard a muffled grunt, a groan, as they landed falling, on the other side — probably on each other. Then he heard the clatter of booted feet crunching across packed snow. As he slumped to the ground he could hear their running footsteps receding in the distance.

"Git up, boon! We can't stay here! The MP's 'll write us up shore as hell and give the battalion a bad name!" The voice sounded heavily labored and strained to Paul's ears, as though the mouth was split — which it was: the tongue foggled, coherence lacking, only the intensity of the moment; a muttering but coming through to his muddled senses loud and clear — although confusing in its purport.

"But they'll help us," Paul protested, imagining them to be the Ninth Cavalry, the Posse, the main body of the Army's Expeditionary Forces coming to their aid. "We can tell 'em what happened!"

"We can tell 'em shit!" Kendall's anger overrode his soreness. In one fleeting instant he looked at Paul as though his friend's naïveté was utterly repugnant to him. Yet, solicitously, he subdued it somewhat. Right now time was of the essence. "I know them motherfuckers a heap better'n you ever will! C'mon, I know a place to hide. C'mon!"

Paul looked defeated. What were "right" and "justice" and "faith" *for,* if one didn't believe those qualities would emerge triumphant in the *end?* Kendall *must* be wrong. Still, something told him that he was not. Some intuitiveness, some hunch, something so obvious as the broken nose now splattered across his face. There was a sense of urgency, in the fullest meaning of the word. He felt he *had* to trust him, no matter what he himself believed.

He allowed himself to be dragged up, weary and sore as he was, and together they stumbled, recovered, rose at a point just barely away from the lights of the oncoming jeep, near a wire gate virtually hidden in the overhanging foliage of the pressing shop. In spite of his body's feeling so completely beaten that death alone stood as a welcoming eminence, his brain admired Kendall's methodicalness in his swift and certain acts: sweeping their pete caps from the ground, pulling him through the nearly invisible gate, closing it shut as noiselessly as possible, then spreading the evergreen foliage thickly and artistically back into place. Kendall ducked Paul's head under the foliage as the jeep neared the wall, and under cover of the jeep's noise dragged the wavering Paul to the softest parts of the grass as soundlessly as a cat's tread, toward the rear of the store. They crawled to the culvert where the peasant women washed the soldiers' clothes at the running stream.

He made Paul lie down near him on the soft part of grass, where the recent snows had disappeared because of so much walking. Made him lie straight — as he himself, did — on his stomach, near the culvert, just this side of the building, where they could both peer out, beyond a small-holed, (thank God!) brick latticework, at the MP's jeep. The two patrolmen embarked, warily alert: one played a searchlight around the area about them, where the assault had taken place. (For some stupid reason Paul closed his eyes, and Kendall, completely in charge now, felt the gesture and nudged his friend viciously.) The two of them then watched these two authoritative peace officers of the Army move stealthily about their rounds.

Beyond a doubt they were white. Both of them knew there were no colored MP's in the provost marshal's section. That went without saying. But they scanned their height level to read something passive or impassive in their faces. They couldn't: the light was too diffuse, too undependable.

They saw more legs than anything. Controlled, directed, alert; feet ready to pivot and descend. In spite of their wounds, their pains, they were quiet as mice when the cat's about, hardly daring to breathe. After an interval of a minute or so of seeing nothing, they could hear talking in fits and starts. Kendall nudged Paul to make sure he was awake and wise to the "happenings" rather than defeated and resigned.

". . . somethin' damn sure was goin' on . . ."

". . . you ain't bull-shittin' . . . some kind of a fight, that's fer sure. . . . Shine your light here!"

". . . those bastards from Ordnance, prob'ly . . ."

"Yeah . . . wonder who called?"

"Beats the hell out of me. . . . They sure got away in a hurry."

"You ain't a-bird-turdin' . . . musta took their wounded wid 'em." Grins nervously. Facetious.

". . . prob'ly." Dryly. Their tension is more apparent than that of those who lie in wait.

". . . GI's a sonofabitch, ain't he? Thinkin' all the time. I *know* these wuz GI's. I kin smell 'em."

". . . Yeah . . . Somethin's wrong here . . . I kin still smell the funk, the talcum. It's too rich, too *clean*. . . . Naw, somethin' ain't right. . . . But I don't *see* a damn thing, do you?"

"Shit, naw. . . . Reckon they scaled this wall and lit out." Peeps through opening. "Je-sus, the snow looks black out there!"

"Fuck it." Disgustedly. ". . . ain' no use lookin' fer ghosts."

"You ain' bull-shittin'." Resignedly, then suddenly contemplative: "Wunder if they wuz any niggers in it?"

Almost too quickly, explaining: "Not hardly. There seems to be a gentleman's agreement with them not to be down here after dark."

Apprehensive, calculating: "See any difference in the blood spots? They tell me a nigger's blood is thicker and darker — like, maroon-colored." Looks.

". . . naw. Look's like plain ol' peckerwood's blood to me."

"Then, on the other han', could be some of them civilians. Commies or some'pin'."

"Yeah. Maybe."

"Everything's quiet, now."

"Shore is. . . . Fuck it, let's go."

"Just say we investigated a disturbance that somebody called in and let it go at that, huh?"

"Damn right. 'Les' you want to go over to Ordnance and have the O.D. and C.Q. make a midnight bed-check."

"Fuck no! They'll think it's a peter parade or some'pin' and I don' wanna go fer that shit!"

"Me neither, come on."

The warriors watched them depart, saw their legs walk past their view. Paul strained his sore head and swelling eyes to get a good glimpse of their figures and faces, so that he would remember them again. The close latticework hindered it. He watched their legs carry them to the jeep and ducked his head back with Kendall as the lights made a sweeping arc about the perimeter once more, then, slowly, made a U-turn and headed in the general direction of town. The governed jeep made a loud noise that wasn't speed at all, just an authoritative sound. But it had saved their lives. He felt they had been that close to extinction.

He was sore *all over!* Especially around his chest. Yet his mind was working forty miles to the minute, his now quieted spirit conscious of the craziest thing: the soft, sibilant sounds the perpetually running stream made—the water lapping over the banks of the dam, flowing down the culvert of the little brook. It seemed the most magnanimous sound for this silent night, holy night. It was like Thoreau's Walden Pond. Hell, it was like the little pond at Kendall's house: so peaceful, gentle, serene. The ground was cold and his fingers were feeling numb and, oddly, the rippling of the stream was balsamic.

With the jeep's sound lost in the distance, they crawled to the edge of the brook's concrete banks. They viewed the now quiet world through the latticework as they approached it.

"All is calm, all is bright." Paul mumbled softly to Kendall as the moon came out, now completely unfettered, and shone brightly in their midst.

"You're damned right it is. And you're alive, I see," his friend encouraged him.

Kendall dipped a handkerchief into the cold black water, mopped his face with it, grimacing succinctly. He dipped it again, repeating the process, blatantly cursing, issuing the sweetly familiar vulgate epithets of Negro troubles, the expressions sounding sardonically humorous and even strengthening to Paul as he listened. The battle was over and both of them — by some whim or fate or chance — were alive and could make some sport of it, no matter how painfully difficult it was to do so.

Kendall sloshed the rag about Paul's face several times. It stung and shocked and even threatened to drown him. Anything to keep him from falling asleep, Kendall thought. There was the danger. Paul protested and bitched mightily and Kendall "rolled." Even Paul laughed. He couldn't help himself. The sight of Kendall rolling on the icy cold ground, slapping it with the palm of his hand, was so awesomely comical he quickly forget about his pains. He had to do something: this fool was going to do with a rag and some water what the white folks hadn't been able to do with *all* their savage kicks and blows!

Revived, sore as they were, Kendall led the way back through a seldom used trail. It led through a line of small cemeteries. Paul winced, remembering the ancient "isms" of Negroes being afraid to go through cemeteries at night. But Kendall's purposefulness in getting them out of danger and into safety *demanded* that he put such fears to flight. Why had he waited so long in life to find a Negro man with such courage, and why had all those beautiful ideals he expounded so brilliantly in the I&E classrooms deserted him so completely in the darkness of night in quiet graveyards? Why did the ancient "isms" make him think that spirits of people long gone would rise up wispily and scare the be-jabbers out of him because it was wrong to intrude upon their sacred ground — he who had virtually been born in church and who revered the gospels; he who had picked his own biblical hero, Paul, his own namesake, in making his First Communion: the thirteenth chapter of the First Corinthians? Now he realized that the man had also written "All things are lawful." Yet he was being led by a man who took the lawful and the expedient as they came and let the devil himself take the hindmost, at times dragging him through other graveyards through the moon's mist, past the suddenly arising crosses that they couldn't help but touch in their staggering walk. He knew that without weapons they couldn't stand another attack, knew that Kendall was ever so determinedly taking him to the numbered safety of house and home, where people loved them and could bathe their wounds and make them well again. And yet he was cringing in fear because they were trespassing upon the real estate of the dead.

How could he let this man down with fear of that sort? It wasn't to be done. Not now. Not ever. So he stumbled on, felt himself being dragged, jerked upright, falling with him, rising, proceeding on, on, on, to the most marvelous sight on the face of the earth: Kendall's house.

They virtually fell into the room. Erika, who was a light sleeper when Kendall was out on the town, awakened with a start, ready to light into her man with verbal tongue-lashings. But when she clicked the light on and saw not one man but two, and both of these bloody and battered, their clothes filthy, her hand went to her throat in shocked horror. Conservative as the Europeans were about fuel, she started a fire immediately. While it was kindling she came over to them to view worriedly their appearance. They looked pitiable. It seemed a toss-up to her, as she looked from one to the other, which was in worse shape. It was Paul. Kendall dragged him to the bed and propped him up there, trying to get the tie loosened from his throat. Erika meanwhile was loosening Kendall's, getting her hands in under his long, busied arms to do so, observing the swollen cheeks, the smashed nose, the split mouth, the large, swollen mouse about the right eye. "Git the cognac, honey," Kendall ordered through thick lips as he hustled Paul's Ike jacket off and started to unbutton the shirt. Erika, bringing the cognac over to Kendall, looked on in puzzled awe. As Kendall unstoppered the bottle with his teeth, grimacing as he did so (they were knocked loose), he pushed the neck of it into Paul's mouth and tilted it up, forcing him to swallow. Then Kendall pulled the bottle away while Paul gagged on the substance for which he normally had to make mental and physical preparations. Kendall took a big drink, waited an instant as it coursed down his throat, and appeared to feel instantly better. He took another. Erika frowned, but said nothing. (Another time she would have called him a pig but now, no.) He handed the bottle back to her without a word. The thing Paul observed most was this rare attitude of Erika's: whereas before she had seemed so bossy, so much the head of this house, she now seemed both astonished and infused with servile humility.

Kendall pushed Paul back on the bed. His eyes looked glassy. The cognac was eliminating some of his ashy pallor. He protested uselessly as Kendall attempted to pull his trousers off, unloosening his belt as Erika bent to pull off the half-boots. It was to no avail. Kendall was in complete charge and with Erika's help soon had Paul's trousers and O.D. shirt off. They both looked at the brown-skinned body with startled apprehension.

The body looked terrible. A rib on his lower left side threatened to protude through the skin at any instant. Welts here and there arose and throbbed, swelled to the body's surface like thick embossing on a sheet of paper. Kendall suddenly undid the shorts, pulled them down. Erika gasped, bringing her hands to her throat. One side of the scrotum had swollen to twice its normal size. The colors on Paul's skin clashed: brown, blue, mauve. Kendall stood silent for a moment, as though weighing the seriousness of it. His concerned expression revealed the seriousness of what he saw. There was nothing much they could do here. The abrasions went too deep. They couldn't fake it. Much more had to be done. X-rays, doubtless. There might be more broken ribs, more internal injuries.

"Honey, go git 'Chili.' "

"Chili" was Sergeant Moment's own personal jeep driver. Short, taciturn, almost self-effacing, one of the few "saintlied" soldiers in the battalion, he lived just three houses down from Kendall. He was a devout, God-fearing, chapel-going man, and fortune, as it reimburses its believers in life, had provided him with a raven-haired mate a scant half-inch shorter than he. (Indeed, they were so much alike in temperament and character that when she wore high heels, she made damned sure that the difference in height was upon her "Chili"—even if she had to search all over town for "short high-heels.") His real name was Lorenzo Marvin Prince, and he was a corporal. His home was Lafayette, Louisiana, and he had been nicknamed "Chili" all his days.

Erika had no trouble finding him. Not addicted to serious drinking, "Chili" was always "home" before midnight. Since Christmas was observed so differently over here than in America — the celebrations commencing one minute after six P.M. on the 25th — "Chili" had gone through the yuletide rituals with the woman he unfailingly referred to as his "wife," Hansi. The trio had come back to Kendall's house and watched him as he put cold compresses on Paul's scrotum, all of them observing the tip of the rib that threatened to poke through at any moment. Kendall virtually ordered "Chili" to get no one but Sergeant Moment and to get him over fast! One look at the suffering I&E man on Kendall's bed was enough for "Chili" to take off without any questions. The only enlisted man in the battalion with authority to carry a jeep off post — and keep it — during after-duty hours, Corporal Lorenzo M. Prince speeded forth to Battalion Headquarters. (To all intents and purposes, Corporal Prince was a courier and a courier was on duty twenty-four hours a day. If need be, Sergeant Moment could cite military authorities. So far, there had never been any need. Sergeant Moment's word *was* authority and *that* authority was *lawful.*)

"Chili" wasn't gone thirty minutes before the assemblage at Kendall's house heard the sound of a jeep and the heavier sound of another vehicle: an ambulance. Sergeant Moment was the first in the room, followed by Corporal Leonard J. McNair, a medic from Washington, D.C., who had flunked out of Howard Medical School for "improprieties." As "Chili" entered, Hansi, a striking, petite brunette, wearing a housecoat over some jeans, closed the door. McNair and Moment stepped over to Paul and, after McNair's intense yet perfunctory examination, uttered without looking at anyone: "We've got to get him to the hospital right away. He's in bad shape."

"Chili" volunteered to help McNair. They wrapped Paul in a

mountain of Army blankets, placed him on a stretcher, loaded him in the ambulance McNair had driven down.

Concerned, Erika reminded them of Kendall. McNair took one look at the Quasimodoish-looking face and said, "Come on, you too." Kendall's protests went unheeded as the entire entourage of that holy night headed toward the ambulance, its motor still idling, the white steam thickly rising in the frosty air. Sergeant Moment, Corporal McNair, and the two patients hastily left the section of Spook Village and headed toward the main road, while "Chili," Hansi, and Erika were left behind, wondering curiously.

Kendall explained the entire sequence of events to Sergeant Moment as the ambulance sped toward the area hospital some fifteen kilometers distant. McNair had given Paul an injection, more against a freezing body-temperature than against the pain. The patient had fallen into a fitful quiet. Sergeant Moment's face was a mask of stifled revulsion.

"Six of the bastards, huh?"

"*Was* six. Merritt broke one's jawbone and the sneaky motherfucker got his hat."

"That's good. He'll have to go to a dispensary, then to a hospital. Then we'll know who the rest of them are — or were. From Ordnance, you think?"

"Pretty sure. It wuz dark and we wuz battling so fast, but they hit that fence that's in back of Ordnance, going that way."

"It's a good thing you had the presence of mind to get him and you back to the village. If the MP's had of picked you up back there you'd have still been back there suffering. To say nothing about writing up a bunch of charge sheets."

"Well, sarge, I know how they operate. We wuz jes' lucky they didn't catch us."

Sergeant Moment scowled and said, "Bastards." His favorite cuss word. The only one anyone ever heard him use. And yet it sounded strange in the ears of the listeners, primarily because everyone in the battalion knew that Sergeant Moment was a homosexual (a white man's word; it didn't really tell a Negro anything. In the Negro vernacular, the man was a stone fag). It was the sibilant way he said "bastards" that shook people a little bit. As though by his saying it heads could *really* roll, whereas one of them saying it was just another cuss word thrown on the wind, accomplishing nothing. They knew however that his revulsion was at the injustice that provoked the word. It was conceivable that some white "bastards" had attacked two members of his race and he was mad as hell about it.

"Paul," he asked, pointing, "a good fighter?" Kendall observed he said "Paul" and not "Merritt."

Kendall's smile was grotesque in the semi-darkness. "One of the best." He laughed suddenly. "He really slammed it on that guy's jaw: ViiiiVIP! He gave as much as he took. One while there I thought we wuz gonna whup 'em all!"

Sergeant Moment smiled. Kendall's one good eye saw that it was one of pride. Even McNair turned around to look at him, with the same kind of smile on his face.

"Some heads are gonna roll behind this, mark my words." The sergeant then turned to look at McNair's head. "Step on it, Mac," he said angrily.

"Right," McNair answered, speeding up, the road in front clear, cool-looking, as only a cold winter's night could look. "We'll be there in a few short ticks." The eloquently cultured voice now sounded strangely colloquial.

They were the only emergency case there — so far. The Officer of the Day, a medical doctor with the rank of captain, came to look over the two soldiers. He glanced at Kendall, attempting to examine him first — at which Kendall referred him to Paul, now prostrate on the examining table. "Get him first, Captain — if you please, suh!"

The officer looked rebukingly at Kendall, whose eyes returned him stare for stare, saw the unmovability of it, saw also the equally serious, equally authoritative expression in Sergeant Moment's face, then moved over to Paul. He pulled the blankets back and saw the jutting rib; then his eyes hastily scanned the rest of the abused body, and seeing the wounds, welts, abrasions, his face suddenly flushed with professional concern. "Medic!" he shouted to the open door. A sound of running feet was heard coming in their direction.

"Get this man ready for surgical examinations! X-rays, and I want plenty of them!"

"Yes, sir," the white medic answered.

The captain looked over at Kendall, saw the battered face, the filthy clothes. "Get your clothes off. Get on the other table."

Kendall began to undress.

"May I assist you, Captain?" McNair's voice: cultured, refined, smooth.

"He's our medic," Sergeant Moment said, as though that explained McNair's status completely.

The doctor looked at him skeptically. "Are you a pill-pusher or something of a doctor?" he asked, blandly.

"At present, a pill-pusher, primarily. To be sure. And yet, something of a doctor, as well."

The doctor stared at him, appraising. "All right." Resignedly. "I'm going to need some help, anyway."

Kendall smiled broadly. Sergeant Moment beamed.

Sergeant Moment helped them move the two oscillatory tables together, placing the two battlers together again, side by side. Sergeant Moment stepped back a discreet distance as the stern-seeming doctor and the washed-out medical student began to apply the medical ways of man to put new life back into damaged bodies. Fatigue suddenly overcame Kendall and a familiar noise was heard by the interested probers: Kendall was asleep and snoring loudly. The group paused to look at the disfigured nose spreading over the swollen face. Sergeant Moment frowned. McNair looked perplexed, the white medic startled. The surgeon shook his head and smiled.

"So . . . I've got two heroes tonight," he said to the sergeant-major, with light aplomb. "Or — maybe two fools."

The sergeant-major's stern countenance broke into a wide grin.

Jean

The one I met, walking,
Without rouge, lipstick, hair un"pressed"
(just good-groomed)
Dark-skinned, black (like me), tall,
Swivel-hipped, clean-looking, pretty,
High-breasted, big-behinded,
Large, expressive eyes, long,
Big shapely legs, feminine gait,
Feminine woman, my kind:
Thirty-four, twenty-six, thirty-eight,
(Hips, by God!)

I, late for work — but getting there —
Anxious like a dog.
Anxious, earning this day, needing it
(more than ever, now)
Having the knowledge that
This poor, unhandsome slob
Loved her — loved her to the teeth.
Right now!

Maybe her bus will stop —
Stop by the barbershop —
At the end of the evening
Discharging passengers,
And she will alight
Fresh as a daisy, ending the day.
Maybe I'll be there,
Bump into — "excuse me" —
Tell her "I'm sorry,"
Contend with a frown,
Get a smile in return.

Walk to the corner
Slowly behind her,
Look like a fool,
Wait for the whispers
To tell me I'm wrong.
Then, free myself from
Such didactic cowardice
And think of some minister
In a Baptist church.

Some Notes on the Frederick Douglass Writers' House

It took me forty years to find this house.

From my lusty, infantile wailings at the foot of my mother's cotton sack in a long, dusty, cotton field in Temple, Texas, to a "suburban" ghetto section of Houston's Fourth Ward, to a riot-torn area of Los Angeles' South Side, often unaffectionately called Watts. It's a good thing, I suppose, that I was a wailer then, because the time was going to come when I would put all that wailing to use and be a writer-to-be among writers-to-be, virtually nesting in the same sort of house in which I was born, and similar to the one in which I was raised! If this is poetic justice then, the justice — delayed as it is, to me — must somehow be fitting.

The first twenty years were kind of normal: that is, for a black man, being poor and what not. Doing chores at home after school — and were they many! Reading storybooks and the Bible and poems from Whittier, Poe, and Robert Service to the aged and infirm, as well as to many illiterate, direct descendants of slaves, plus making damn near any kind of hustle to get a few bucks to help keep our family going. Shining shoes, for instance, at five cents a pair (I made a young mint on weekends!), throwing handbills on Friday evenings for grocery stores (now such things are corporations), selling the Houston *Chronicle* and *Post* on a secondhand bicycle — bought with extreme thrift — on Saturday nights and early Sunday mornings. Always keeping one eye open for malicious white drunks in speeding cars, threatening to run us over; young white boys, our own ages, who traveled in gangs and beat the snot out of us when we were too slow of foot or wheel; and the ever-prevalent "boys in blue" who called us "nigger" with varying timbres of voice, which, by knowing, and by knowing how to "act" in those strange, unfamiliar white areas, prevented some severe head-whippings.

Then I was eighteen and off to the wars — bless the Saviour — although in a segregated army, company, battalion. Having a freedom that was not really a freedom but which contained some helpfully lusty incentives within the interlude and the varied climes where it was my fortune to be stationed. Here, in my ever-searching solitudes, did I become more associated with books, thinkers, and writers of books. Even here, my old adolescent processes of reading and knowing and remembering stood me in good stead. There were many I met along that way, in that war, who desired with all their hearts to know what there was to be known. Many who had "escaped" their own miserable Southern hamlets, even as I; many from the canebrakes, the cotton patches, the eternal "sharecropping," the muddy Mississippis, and the aloof and lifeless ghettos, who came, *willingly,* as conscripts to serve — however, supposedly, "utilitarian" — as soldiers in this war that was to end *all* wars. Now I had a built-in, within-me sort of freedom: some call it perspective. I *still* call it freedom. *I* could help those who wanted to caress words, sentences, paragraphs — their meanings — to their bosoms, and to feel that they walked in a knowledgeable light and that once they learned, they possessed a power that prevented them from ever returning to the yoke of ignorance and a borrowed plow simply because of ignorance alone, and that they could go on from there in pursuit of other greater knowledge and, consequently, more comfortable living.

I must have been the most "natural" teacher the world has ever known. I sure didn't have any degrees. Didn't have a diploma, even, then. (That came later, via a lot of correspondence courses and things.) All I really had was zeal, interest, enthusiasm. I guess *they* needed *that*. I had a good memory. I wasn't afraid to face a class and give a lesson. I suppose necessity overrode fear — in this case. And I was young. That helped. My reputation for studiousness always seemed to precede me somehow from camp to camp. I wasn't a catalyst — I don't think — but I was often called on to work in anything that *taught*. As a consequence I continued to seek out more knowledge, to know and to observe.

My horizons broadened with these now anchored-in incentives. I even stayed in the military longer because of the continuing traveling, because the desire to know things seemed to ever rekindle itself. And, like the Big Bear making his big strides across the Milky Way, I felt like the baby bear making some baby strides across continents other than this one — with the help of a journeying, military mendicant. I was its foil to hawk her wares. I was one of its musician sentinels, who often doubled in brass, from trumpet to trombone, it seemed, from one coda to the next as the symphonic pages were turned. Because for every area we halted in to hawk our military wares I found or established a symbol of learning for those other black masses in my midst who wanted to improve their minds and thereby destroy the myth that intelligence and learning only favored a few.

In this all-black, military world with which I was associated for nearly eight years was another, historical black world that existed in musty, black-imbued books in segregated camps, in post and station libraries. We found many black heroes there: Harriet Tubman, Frederick Douglass, Booker T. Washington, Alexandre Dumas, and many, many others. They were fiery spokesmen, natural-born rebels, lovers of freedom, abolitionists. I wrote for, of, and about the comrades in my midst because there was seldom anyone else in our immediate group who could do so or who *would* do so. It boosted my morale while elevating theirs. It established my ultimate aims while infusing them with a status quotient to their immediate worlds that were so many-faceted and important — just like their own white brothers in their many white camps. Suddenly, reading and knowing and the desire to impart knowledge of things that were, that came before, that came afterwards, became all-encompassing. Suddenly I *knew* what I wanted to do most of all: I wanted to communicate. Dammit! I wanted to write!

Then I was back in Houston again. The traveler at home to rest. The chicken to roost. Now for the assembling of thousands of notes and minute impressions. Now the collecting of past fires and often repressed heats. (Now the aura of various syntaxes abounded before me, above the clouds, beneath my pillow, in the demeanor of people in my midst, in the trouble of black folk everywhere. In an Alabama bus-boycott, a poem; in the merciless slaughter of black innocents in Sharpesville, Africa, a poem; in a white youth's spitting in a young Negro girl's face at a university, a poem; in the senseless lynching of a Negro man, a poem; in the senseless castration of a Negro man on a lonely Southern road, with his love, his woman, a poem, an epistle, a decree; in the wanton killing of a Negro soldier in a German field a story: in a collective round-up of many incidents, involving many colored people and many people of color, from many provocations, many aggrandizements, many frustrated attempts of many black people to rise above the now stereotyped status of the lowly, a book, a huge book, to ever trumpet to the world. And more stories, a play, an essay, an article. The written word. The word. *Im die eingang vor dass wort.* In the beginning was the word. A surfeit of impressionable tidbits that flit across my mind's eye from time to time, and I feel the need to commit it all to paper.

The rejection slips come back almost faster than I can send these missives out. Too late. Too early. Doesn't fit in with our current needs. Sorry. Sorry. Sorry. Some, never to return. Some irretrievably lost. Other bits of knowledge gained from bumming around so many libraries flash across my mind's eye during these last ten years at home, causing me to ponder: Writers' Conference, Breadloaf, Martha's Vineyard. Places so far away. Writing groups that are held together by one common bond: to communicate. The wonderment if such places are exclusively *white* or if open only to *published* Negro writers. An impasse looms.

New Negro writers on the horizon: now here, now there. One, extremely gifted, each new work of his better than the last: *Go Tell It on the Mountain, Notes of a Native Son, Nobody Knows My Name, Another Country.* A sudden glance in a bookstore reveals yet another racial face on the cover of another epistle, some ten years in the doing, with a highly provocative title: *A Chosen Few.* There are others, yet distant from here. How did they start getting *their* works published? What simple quirk of fate turned their blinking amperes into blazing kilowatts? What the hell did publishers want?

The laboring goes on. It has to. I am too much past the point of no return. I am too deeply committed to my calling. The little construction jobs that perpetuate my existence are few and far between. They don't pay enough, nor do they last. Where I was naïve and subservient in my formative years, I am belligerent and filled with aggression now. I've got to help kill the cursed stereotypes rather than docilely sustain them. Nip them in the bud at the outset. This is dangerous because it is believed to be anti-social on my part. So I often lose that which I urgently need more than the mere publishing of a manuscript.

The years pass. The people die. Both of them. The mother and the father. Their youngest son's only accomplishment before their deaths is a full-page, complete-spread story and photo of me and my frustrating attempts at getting my work published. They read that an excerpt from my play, *Bye, Bye, Black Sheep,* has been put on in a local theater. They read of my numerous other works and are startled because I could never issue these declarations before and truly *convince* them. At last, at least, they are proud of this. Because writing is an intangible thing. No one can *see* a writer *writing* like they can see a sculptor *sculptoring,* a painter *painting,* a pianist *piano-ing*. Writing is a gift that completely envelops the intellect and keeps it hidden, until the testaments are blazoned on papers of the world, if the penman is thus lucky. It keeps its adherents studious. Some may prefer a beard to build an image, but on me it scratches. I'm an introvert and easily touched anyway: for true impressions or false ones. My successes or failures have to be worked out by me from there on.

Finally, after ten years of this futility, my first cousin, who has longed to see me in the twenty years we've been apart, sends for me. I hesitate, dreading to leave home, and especially those that I hold dear — the midway mark of forty fairly whistling around the corner — to come to this place, to L.A. And, ultimately to Watts. Reluctantly, I go.

Here my chances for survival alone are eight million to one. Seven times greater than at home. Gregariousness abounds. In a sea of people is a man alone here. They rush to and fro. The forest is too thick to see the trees. Jobs that appear on the surface to be magnanimous and lasting fade out before I can get solidly entrenched. This is a big town, with big-town ways and with big-town temper. I arrive here on the last night of the Watts upheaval. A terrible time for a Southerner with limited laboring skills to be job-hunting. Occasionally I ride a bus out to Watts to view the havoc's remains. The ghetto that still exists reminds me of the one I left behind, only mine was infinitely smaller in size — but not degree. Actually I feel a kinship, an almost natural metamorphosis, as though I've been here all along. In spirit I have. I know I'll be back.

During my ramblings while trying to establish myself as a citizen here, I locate a former friend from home: David Westheimer. He is doing very well with his latest book, *Von Ryan's Express,* which has now become a movie. He helps me out considerably. (Thank God for the David Westheimers of this world!) He impresses upon me the need to join the Budd Schulberg Writers' Class. I remember this guy's works. I had read *What Makes Sammy Run?* and *The Disenchanted.* Had seen the "The Harder They Fall" and "On The Waterfront" as movies. At the time, it seemed incongruous to me that he was heading a writers' group in Watts, or anyplace else for that matter. I don't know why. I didn't want to be taught how to write. I knew how to do that. I wanted to be taught how to be *published.* Of course I didn't know the set-up. I was in an economic fog. I let David's suggestion ride a while, meantime becoming familiar with Los Angeles and trying to keep the wolf of starvation from my door.

It was a bitch all the way. This place is colder than an Eskimo's nose in the Klondike. It's amazing how the many Southern people that one meets here change so radically within the flux of a big city's momentum. There were more people of the earth here, just like me, who beat me out of my few pitiful shekels from my hard labors, than one could shake a stick at — and who then got swallowed up in the vastly tentacled mires of L.A.! My landlord and I were perennially at loggerheads over *his* rent money. At one point I slept in my car for five nights — straight! (But they were very tolerant, very considerate with me and my shenanigans. I don't owe them as much money now as I do gratitude.) The only collateral I had for subsistence during my acute joblessness was my typewriter, my veritable right arm with which to solicit work. I pawned it — as though pawning my soul! — to carry me over to another hopeful day that did not bring much hope. But I hopped, skipped, jumped, loped over many minor jobs to scrape up that twenty-five bucks to get it back. I think hell itself will have to freeze over before I go that route again.

During another visit to David Westheimer's "writing house" he gave me a copy of his latest book, *My Sweet Charlie,* and repeated the suggestion that I attend Schulberg's writing class. This time I didn't hesitate. From that first day I knew that it was to such a group as this that I had always wanted to belong.

We were given an assignment. "What caused the riots?" and "Would they occur again?" — all in conjunction with our writing skills and the Poverty Program. When our works were turned in and assessed by Budd Schulberg it was considered apt material for filming a documentary. It was titled "The Angry Voices of Watts." Stuart Schulberg, the producer, presented in beautiful, pictorial prose the very essence of the inequities of which we wrote. My works — as well as those of the rest of the class — were at last published.

Then, a house *for* writers was leased, with the prime intention of establishing it as a place for talented writers to live and pursue their craft in, particularly those with "no visible means of support" who are otherwise exposed to the stigma of colossal drifting and the woeful anxieties of repressed communication. I see it in this light because *I* was once a drifter. And God knows, I've been entombed in that "no visible means of support" bag many times over. But the most endearing part of this gesture by Budd Schulberg, and other men of his stamp, is that of all the Arts, the one that is the *least* concrete especially among members of *my* race, *this* one, that of writing creatively, has at last been given some recognition.

As for the house itself, it was no fabulous pad by even a writer's stretch of imagination. It was certainly one from *my* past. It had been thoroughly lived in and just needed some "fixing." Actually, it might have been the type of house that Frederick Douglass himself lived in, pursued his dream of freedom in, was closeted in to learn the alphabet and — consequently — to be a master of the written and uttered word. And I was given a chance to work on it and in it, to help shape it up to some comfortable degree of livability.

This is probably the first house of its kind in history, and I, for one, am certainly glad it's here. Now our present writers' group, to which I am happy to belong, will hold our meetings here, read our works, old and new, and share our knowledge of outlets to which to send our labored testaments across the land.

We are all in accord with the zealousness of that symbolic man, Frederick Douglass, who taught himself to read and commit his thoughts to paper, enjoining us to become equally zealous, now solidified in our unity — and ever hoping by our conjoined efforts to help improve the ills of the world, and of the black man in particular, by shouting our declarations to the world. Indeed, to the whole universe!

FANNIE CAROLE BROWN

was born in March, 1942, in New Orleans, Louisiana, and graduated from school there in 1959. She was editor-in-chief of the school paper, *The Tiger,* which won both local and national awards. She attended Bradley University in Peoria, Illinois, with a major in speech correction. Then in 1961 she moved to California, worked at the Pasadena Post Office, and with the help of her mother, began selling real estate. Having received various awards in speech and oratorical contests, she got a job in the Theatre Americana's (Altadena) production of Roy Bush's *Two Daughters.* For her performance in this she won the Theatre Americana's statuette for Best Actress of the Year. Meanwhile, she put together a book of verse which won a literature award in 1965 from the National Council of Negro Women. She is a regular member of the Writers' Workshop, having joined it in the fall of 1966.

The Realization of a Dream Deferred

It happened; a success
Why then do I remain emotionless?

From beneath many a strata —
  Strata of bewilderment
  Strata of disillusionment
  Strata of lost hope
  Self-pity
  Self-doubt
It bursts forth.

And now
It has happened; a success
But why do I yet remain emotionless?

Lullaby, My Son

Close your eyes, my darling one,
Sleep sweetly while you may;
Dream of tomorrow's cycle ride
And the ice-cream cake today.

For all too soon it's over,
That sweet sleep of today.
Tomorrow only holds despair
That sleep won't take away.

So close your eyes, my darling one,
May He be at your side;
The day you know my sorrow
May He yet remain your guide.

DAVID REESE MOODY

DAVID REESE MOODY was born in December, 1933, in Pasadena, California, where his father was a postal worker. He was educated in Pasadena, and took an Associate in the Arts degree from Pasadena City College, after which he was married. He was in the Air Force for four years. "Then there was my flight from the security of Pasadena," he says, "to the chaos of the South Los Angeles jungle, when I realized that personal dignity does not come easily." He has held various jobs and is a former prize fighter who still works out with professional heavyweights at Jake Sugrue's Gym in South Los Angeles.

Consequence

It was two-thirty and Friday morning. I entered my home with a light step as a result of the four Jack Daniels I had consumed at Marty's, where the jazz was, and to prevent waking my family.

In my search of the kitchen (where the food is kept) I discovered in the sink a large black bug. A bug about one and one-quarter inches in length and five-eights of an inch in width, with two uncommonly long antennae projecting from his forehead. I assumed the bug to be male because he looked male. Let's call him Sam. The sink is divided into two parts, one side with a garbage disposal and the other with a regular drain. Sam happened to be in the side with the regular drain. The glacier-like whiteness of the Ajax-polished surface gave Sam's blackness and size amplification. Sam was very still, almost as though he was aware of my presence. I observed Sam in quiet contemplation: "Sam is wrong; he's looking to take something from me: what, is of no consequence. Sam is trespassing; Sam means me no good; Sam is possibly a carrier of some disease, if not medical, social." Feeling I needed no more justification I sentenced Sam to death.

I deftly placed the stopper in Sam's side of the sink to cut off the possibility of escape — that is, escape from my vision. The prosecutor has the right to "see" justice done in instances where capital punishment is involved. Using the garbage disposal as an instrument of execution I found it to be inexpedient for the effort of transportation. Sam's great long antennae were rotating like two miniature radars, as though he was now more keenly aware of the imminence of his situation. Like lightning the words "hot water" came to me. The faucet, being of the swivel type, took on the appearance of "The Great Hand of Justice." The hot water had not been used for several hours, therefore to obtain some, it was necessary to let the hot water run for a period of a minute or two. I took "The Great Hand of Justice" in mine and swung it over the side of the sink containing the garbage disposal, then turned the "H" handle to the "on" position, deliberately. In the adjacent chamber Sam began to move, aware of a change in the quiet and of the vibrations emitted by the water and enamel and metal splashing together. When the water temperature reached the lethal point of giving off steam I turned it with absolute conviction into Sam's place. Sam ran at the glacier-like sides of the sink with desperation; all the wrath of justice touched Sam and his bowels ran; there was no way out; in a matter of seconds Sam was overcome. The casket was a paper towel and the remains were laid to rest in the toilet.

It occurred to me that Sam may have had a sister or brother who may have had children, making Sam — Uncle Sam.

EDNA GIPSON was born prematurely in December, 1946, weighing one pound and seven ounces, and spent the first three months of her life in a hospital. She grew up in Watts and went to school there. Handicapped by a severe speech impediment, she "stayed clear of people," and discovered books. She started writing short stories when she was fourteen. In 1965 she enrolled at Los Angeles City College. She first began attending the Watts Writers' Workshop at the Watts Happening Coffee House during the summer of 1966, and became an official member of the group in December of the same year. She is at work on a novel about her generation coming of age in Watts. Her contemporaries in the Workshop consider her "an authentic voice of 103rd Street."

A Deep Blue Feeling

Question: So what happens when all your tricks and games play out and you finally see things as they really are, only it's too late — What do you do?

It had just started to rain when I stepped off the bus; a groovy scene. The sun was a fading yellow, cast against a gray sky, and the slow force of the wind made the leaves of the trees dance frantically. It was a haunting sound. The streets, now wet with rain, glistened in the brilliant gloominess of the day as the dark clouds gathered. The air was fresh and clean, with the smell of autumn. I stood there and I couldn't believe it. I had to reach down and touch things — like the sidewalk and the green wet grass — to make sure the world was really there, and that I was part of it.

Then suddenly, I got this weird sensation that I had to move, had to get to where I was going and fast! Too many of my years had been spent just standing still. For once I had to do something; I had to believe in something. I walked hurriedly through the streets, holding life with my eyes: seeing the faces of people, hearing voices, maybe for the first time *understanding*. I remember saying to myself, "You're going to make it, boy; I mean you're *really* going to make it."

The rain began to soak me and I could see right then that I needed protection, so on went my "shades"; I was cool.

I pushed on for another half a block before this groovy, way-out feeling took hold of me. It's hard to describe. I only know that for the first time in two years I felt this wild sense of freedom . . . the kind of freedom you feel when you're riding in a sports car with the top down. Your head is resting against the back of the seat and you're digging the mellow sounds of John Coltrane or Donald Byrd — the kind of freedom that you feel after blowing pot, or when you're at the park, lying on your back, looking up at the sky, and the birds are screaming their secrets in your ear, and you want to explode! Like Wow!!

I was lost in everything I saw. Simple ordinary things, like clothes lines and traffic lights . . . I mean I was really tripping . . . I guess I must have walked for hours, because when I finally came to myself I was on 99th and Central Avenue. I walked down a few blocks more, crossed and made a left, and suddenly there I was: 103rd Street, in the heart of Watts. I froze.

"Home" in large blue letters flashed across my brain as I stood there weak with mixed feelings of fear and anxiety, and at the same time joy and sadness. I couldn't understand it; I mean, I didn't think I had it in me. But those tears in my eyes and that lump in my throat couldn't have been more real. I was righteously choked up. No shit. Nothing had really changed except a few remodeled houses here and there; but other than that the old neighborhood looked pretty much the same.

Evidence of the riots could still be seen in the form of cold, empty spaces where buildings had once stood, in fragments of blackened bricks and thin, multi-shaped glass. For some reason seeing this didn't affect me one way or the other. I just sort of nodded at its existence. All the bitterness and hate were gone. I turned and saw the roof of my own house in the distance. My heart was beating so hard that it hurt. I had intended to move on but some nameless voice was holding me back. Only seconds later, to my surprise and bewilderment, I was like facing Will Rogers Park. This hit me pretty hard and for a moment or two my mind went blank. I felt it coming, then, as it always did, when things that I couldn't control started happening to me whenever I was in a complete state of helplessness: that deep blue feeling.

I said it to myself and then I said it out loud: "Will Rogers Park," I whispered: "Will Rogers Park." The place where all my troubles began. School was for squares — so I didn't go. Instead I made it to the park and learned everything I thought I needed to know. It was there that I dropped my first benny, blew my first joint, got my first shot of smack (heroin.) Like I was hip.

It all came back to me during those brief pain-tinged seconds as I stood there in the rain, while the wind raged through the trees. I didn't want it to come back. I wanted to close my mind — to forget the old. But one thought led to another. As I closed my eyes I could see the face of my mother. I thought of all the heartbreak and anguish I must have caused her, without knowing it, or even caring. Constantly in and out of jail, not being able to hold a steady job, coming home at all hours, really *wasted!* But those days were over now. A lot had happened to me during those two years I had been away — I'd grown up.

Less than a heartbeat later I was *there,* standing on the front porch of our old broken-down house, looking up at the now-still sky, righteously convinced that life was beautiful and that there was much to do and see and feel. Then my hand was on the doorknob. I turned it slowly and walked in. I saw Mama sitting on the sofa and for a second or two I was like paralyzed. I mean, I couldn't move. I looked around and discovered that nothing had changed.

The little furniture we owned was still scattered about in the same depressing way as it had always been. I hated this room as a kid. I hated it more than any other room in the house because it was the living room, and people *had* to see it — people like the *guys.* They had to see that couch we had, the one with the holes eaten through, exposing that sick-looking cotton. They had to see the matching chair, the one with all four legs missing. The one propped up on those four red bricks. They had to see that picture of Niagara Falls rotting against the wall, and those faded nylon curtains at the windows. They had to see that old-fashioned floor lamp, the one with no shade, and the coffee table that sat in front of the couch — the one with the scratches and cigarette burns. They had to see the plaster peeling off the walls and the gaping holes in the ceiling that somehow never got fixed.

My parents never seemed to get anywhere and that really bugged me. I couldn't understand it. My father had had fairly good jobs and all and we never had any extra-heavy bills to pay, so why couldn't we make it? Why couldn't we get *there?* All through high school, until I quit, I kept waiting for something to happen. I was at the age when things really began to affect me. Things like the colors of autumn, or the store fronts down 103rd Street. I began exploring beyond my little world into the realms of other people's worlds — through books and plays, through motion pictures and music. I started getting involved in some of my classes at school, and then suddenly came my discovery: I could *paint!* I don't think I have ever been more excited than I was then, because deep within me I *knew* that this was what I had been searching for, I guess all my life. Something to justify my being born, a goal, a destination; and now I had found it.

I left my old crowd and began doing things on my own: like going to art galleries and museums. Or to the free concerts they gave every Sunday at Exposition Park. Or to the main Public Library downtown.

These things started happening all at once and it was just too much for me, all at once. I had all this energy and vitality and every day was like a new day. I had to tell *someone*. If I didn't I was going to explode. I just knew I would.

So I'd go running home after school as fast as I could and head straight for the kitchen where Mama was. This must have happened a million times. I'd stand in the doorway watching her as she cooked, barely able to catch my breath and trembling with uncontrolled excitement. There was so much I wanted her to know, but somehow I could never put it into words. I mean, how do you tell a person that you feel good inside in a particular way, because the sky is a certain color? I'd stand there, it seemed, forever, trying to explain to her all the weird changes I was going through and how groovy it was to be alive and breathing! I'd try to tell her about my classes at school and the books I was reading. I'd try to tell her that I needed things — like a pair of shoes once in a while, a new suit, art supplies. I knew Mama seldom heard me. Her mind was always on something else, like where the rent money for next month was coming from. Yet I kept right on: "Oh, Mama, I want . . . I want . . . Mama, I want EVERYTHING! Tell me what to do!"

I went through a series of part-time jobs after school, hoping that I could save the little money I made and later buy some of the things I needed. But somehow my old man managed to get himself laid off or fired just as I started working. When there was no food in the house. And some bills needed paying. So I never got that easel I wanted so much or that suede sport coat I had in lay-away. And I never made that trip to the Pickwick Book Shop.

Then one morning I woke up and I just didn't care anymore. Because no one else seemed to care, because caring only made you hurt. I stopped waiting and hoping. I stopped running to Mama with my guts in my hand, because she couldn't help me. Nobody could. So forget you ever wanted to paint, boy, forget you've ever read *The Catcher in the Rye,* forget everything, because nothing means nothing! And I did forget everything. The biggest mistake of my life.

The only reason my old man married Mama was because he knocked her up. He never let her or anyone else forget that. Usually people try to keep those things a secret, but not my old man. He told everybody about it. Even me. Everything that happened was always Mama's fault. No matter what it was she was always to blame. He used to fight her a lot, kick her in the stomach, hit her in the head —

he didn't care who was there. He'd do it in front of anybody: me and my friends, Mama's relatives, and once he even did it in front of the Water and Power man — when he came to shut off the lights. He smashed her right across the face. I know. I was there. I saw it all.

But like, what can you do when you're five years old?

EMMERY EVANS was born in High Point, N.C., where he was reared by his grandmother. He stayed in high school an extra year and "part of those five years," he says, "were spent in the city park, lolling on the benches. . . . Some days were spent on the basketball court. The pool hall grew to be like a second school, a club, a family gathering hall. All the guys would meet around the old coal stove and lie about some girl." After high school he went to California. Since then, he says, "I have had a few loves . . . a few successes . . . a few failures. Today I am alone. Today I contemplate the sadness of war, the beauty of love, the supremacy of God. I am a poet." Now in his early twenties, he first came to the Watts Writers' Workshop in the summer of 1966. He is currently a resident of Douglass House.

Love or Life?

From a balcony I yell, arms outstretched, hands singing
aimless songs into the sky; false are the words ringing
from my mouth, aimlessly do they float, though my brain
is expanding.

I think of old women; like Baudelaire I too follow their
grace with my eyes, with my mind; beauty does not tarnish;
it is only the beholder's vision that deceives his mind; old
women, wrinkled from sex, wrinkled from life, wrinkled from
love.

And what might I say of man, since I am condemned to be one?
I cannot say; I only know that I do not know, and I am even
uncertain of this; the world floats around in my brain, it
was conceived there, and it will die there.

A Serpent Smiles

This is for the woman who brought the shades of
sin upon the world, a sin that aches my loins to
this present day. A man and a woman lay in the bushes
sweating with the joys of their newfound love,
while a serpent smiled;

Anger rose as a red cloud in the heavens, while we
poor animals shook with horror; I remember Eve,
lying pompous on her hip, with a tinted flushing smile,
like she was the new heroine of life; all I saw, while a
serpent smiled;

Leaves hide no shame, the wind whispered as they slipped
about; love she said to me, and love I whispered hoarsely
into her ear; winds hurt not my ears with that song. Play
for me a melody light and gay; I am drunk with apples
of which too I was not to partake, all, all; while a
serpent smiled;

This bitter earth, not a soft velvety cloud of green,
but a stone, a stone, a stone, a stone that broke our
backs as we fell, and we too began to slither and crawl;
love, love all through my veins, running through my
head and through my heart, yes, through my heart, and
even yet, a serpent smiles.

In the Name of God

And I am alone again, sitting here with papers
strewn from one end of the table to the other,
craving like some hungry beggar for food, but
it is not food I desire, it is love;
          Feed me love,
   give my hungry heart its nourishment
and if the world is as I preach, a rotted vegetable,
destroy the worms that infest it,
          Dear God, plant a garden anew;
and let the scorpions be tame with love;
          World,
                    World,
                              listen to my plea,
          and benefit from my death, which will
          be soon, but soak not that plot of
          soil lying over my corpse with tears,
          strain not salty molecules for me,
          retire to your cots, hang those sad
          bulging eyes over the pliant sobs; I
          have written,
                            study my form, and linger
          on my words;
          Christ;
          God almighty, deliver my soul from this
          flesh, world beware God's wrath,
          He is mightier than all your puppet armies,
          my mind soars now to a spiritual land,
          and letters fall on to this page, without a
          prior thought on my part,

Sanctus
Sanctus
Sanctus,
yes, holy is His name.

BLOSSOM POWE was born in Saint Louis, Missouri, in June, 1929. Her family moved to Los Angeles in 1931 and stayed there for two years, then returned to St. Louis "financially beaten, but not bowed." In 1937 they went to a farm in Maryland and raised tomatoes and corn for a year. Back in St. Louis again, she started school, and wrote her first poem, "Hallowe'en." By the time she was fourteen, she had a part-time job in a laundry, where her father also worked. When she was fifteen, she and her best friend became chorus girls at the Club Riviera, where many of the great jazz musicians played. She finished school in St. Louis (while living with an aunt) and wrote the valedictory speech for the graduating class. She then joined her family, which had returned to Los Angeles, and soon after was married. She and her husband live in Los Angeles County with their six children. She became a member of the Writers' Workshop in the fall of 1966. "Christmas in the Ghetto" is a section from her novel-in-progress entitled *See What Tomorrow Brings.*

Black Phoenix

And so, each day
Became a nightmare . . .
With no place else to run:
Picket fences falling down,
Sidewalks crumbling on the ground,
Hunger crawling all around . . .
Waiting for tomorrow!
And then Time . . . running swiftly,
Stopped to sift through the ashes
With barely visible picks
And such weak hands —
Crying! Brooding! Trying somehow
To create . . . from dreams archaic . . .
From old edicts and empty places!

And so, each day
Became a nightmare . . .
Torture under the sun:
Picket fences falling down,
Sidewalks crumbling on the ground,
Hunger marching all around . . .
Waiting for tomorrow!
And then Time . . . walking quietly,
Stooped to lift the burnt ashes,
Wondering how it could fix
The broken Bands —
Crying! Brooding! Trying somehow
To create . . . a thing prosaic
From kindling sticks and shoeless laces!

And so, each day
Became a nightmare . . .
But, what is done is done:
Picket fences falling down,
Sidewalks crumbling on the ground,
Hunger running all around . . .
Waiting for tomorrow!
And now, Time . . . crawling slowly,

Starts to sift through the ashes
Of this black kind of Phoenix
With trembling hands —
Crying! Brooding! Trying somehow
To create . . . a new mosaic
From broken bricks and charcoal faces!

What Can I Say?

What can I think
That some black brother
Hasn't thought before . . .
In new dismay
Choking with sorrow
Born of being poor?

What can I say
That some black brother
Hasn't said before . . .
At break of day
Seeking tomorrow
From outside the door?

What can I do
That some black brother
Hasn't done before . . .
Making his way
Through streets too narrow
To tread anymore?

I can think . . . for myself!
I can speak . . . for myself!
I can do for myself!
And, then,
When I stand facing myself
I can do it with pride . . .
Knowing that I have been
True to myself!

Tomorrow

Don't say to us, "tomorrow"
For tomorrow never comes;
It is just a vague diversion
For deceiving simple ones.
Don't tell us to keep waiting
While the bell so sadly tolls
For this "weight" could break the bridges
That link fast our very souls.
Don't say to us, "Move slowly"
For this will never do
(When we all know this sage advice
does not pertain to you!)
Don't tell us to be patient
While the lynch mob's thirsty crew
Carries out a gruesome verdict
'Neath some willow wet with dew.
Don't say to us, "Walk softly.
Don't make noise and don't offend"
While your silence winks at murder
To condone such bloody sin.
And do not say, "I'm sorry"
Then stand back with helpless hands
While the self-styled "undertakers"
Meet to feast in hungry bands.
Please!!!!!!
Don't say to us, "tomorrow"
For tomorrow never comes;
It is just a fool's diversion
Tranquilizing simple ones.

Christmas in the Ghetto

Doors and windows were displaying sparkling ornaments of the season, and trees, heavy beneath their burden of snow and ice, still managed to point their long, artistic fingers to the sky.

At Christmas, a chill fills the air and a warmth fills the heart, for this is the season that revives pleasant memories and brings to mind the days of childhood when the Big City was a huge wonderland reveling beneath a royal cape of snow. But all through the winter and especially at Christmastide there are higher prices to pay for kindling wood and coal, bigger gas bills, increasing costs of food and clothing for the children, and the pain of getting up in the cold, wee hours of morning to go out to work — even when water will not pass through the frozen pipes.

Christmas does not always bring happiness.

There was nothing unusual about Sarah Roberts. She looked like most of the other seven-year-olds who lived in the neighborhood except that perhaps she was a bit more frail. Sarah was a shy, quiet child in spite of the noisy street where she lived.

Ever since she could remember, she had spent most of her idle hours right there on the stoop at the bottom of the stairs that led up to where she lived with her parents, and since it was Christmas Eve she was spending just as much of her time there as the cold out-of-doors would allow. She had on two pairs of thick socks over her long, brown winter stockings, and the faded knit cap she wore was so tight that it was uncomfortable; every once in a while she would tug at the knot under her chin. No matter how she complained about it, her mother always tied it that way! She said that it had to be tight or else she would lose it, the way she lost the other one last winter. So Sarah never said anything about it to her mother anymore. Especially when her mother's eyes were angry the way they had been just before she came down to the stoop.

Sarah wistfully looked at everything that moved up and down the avenue: the automobiles and the streetcars and the people who passed by without even seeming to notice her. She watched the parade of late Christmas shoppers with delight, trying to guess what they carried in their shopping bags and parcels, as her quick eyes took in every detail. Just now, she wanted a drink of water, but she didn't want to go back upstairs. Still, she was thirsty. So she decided to pretend that she wasn't thirsty, at least, for a little while.

Gold's Delicatessen was directly under the flat where she lived, so she looked through the window to see what was going on there. She often watched him waiting on customers. But tonight she could hardly see into the place, the window was so steamed up because of the cold weather. All the same, she couldn't keep from thinking about it. She liked Mr. Gold's Delicatessen. It was one of her favorite places and it always smelled so good . . . like salami and kosher pickles . . . and those windmill cookies. She just loved those windmill cookies. And Mr. Gold was a nice man. Sometimes, when she went into the store, he would give her windmill cookies for free. She liked that . . . but she never liked to actually watch him reach down into the big cookie jar to get them for her, just as she never liked to see him reach into the pickle jar to get a pickle for her. She did not like the long, black, curly strands of hair that grew on his hands and on his fingers. His hands just didn't look right to her. They were too pink and speckled and hairy. He was a very nice man and everything, but she didn't like his hands!

Reluctantly, Sarah went up the dingy, musty-smelling stairs, pausing as she heard her father's strong voice bellowing through the house. He was angry and he was using lots of very bad words. She hadn't heard her mother say anything and she wondered what she was doing and if the day was going to end with another fight.

She peeped into the kitchen.

It was a mess. The day's collection of dirty dishes covered most of the table and the sink was full of pots and pans with black, sooty bottoms. A big plate was in shattered pieces on the floor and the linoleum was caked with dried-up slops. An improvised clothesline hung with drab-colored clothes stretched lazily across the width of the kitchen from wall to wall and sagged into an arch just over the kitchen table.

Sarah looked at her father and then at her mother. They were both drunk. He was standing up and he still had on his hat and his working clothes. He kept on saying bad words to her mother who sat at the table smiling a nasty smile. She didn't seem to be paying any attention to him as she poured herself a drink from the bottle on the table. She reached for the glass and started to get up.

"Why'n't you shuddup?" she suggested to him coldly, lazily.

"Who you telling t'shuddup?" His hand came down hard across her face!

She fell back into the chair again to glare at him with eyes that flashed hate.

Sarah grew very tense as she stood pasted to the wall in the shadows of the dimly lit hall, afraid to make her presence known. She was sorry she had to come upstairs in the first place and her father's voice made her afraid to even move, so she couldn't go back downstairs either. She winced when she heard him strike her mother again.

"That'll teach'ya to watch out what'cha say to me from now on! I'm running things around here!" He snatched the bottle from the table, put it into his overcoat pocket and left the kitchen.

Sarah stood as close to the wall as she could and he rushed by without seeing her. He blew his nose as he went down the steps and mumbled something about never coming back.

From the hall, Sarah could hear her mother crying and gulping down whatever it was that she was drinking.

After a minute, Sarah eased back down the stairs and opened the door to peer out. She didn't see her father anywhere, so she went out and closed the door noiselessly behind her. It felt so good to be outside again that she wished she didn't ever have to go back upstairs . . . Christmas or no Christmas!

She thought that maybe her father was in the delicatessen, but she couldn't tell because of the cloudy window.

Flakes of snow began to fall again and she looked up at the sky, praying that this time Santa Claus would not forget to bring her the things she had asked him for in the big store downtown. The last time, he *had* forgotten, and she had been a good girl, too!

She prayed that this time Santa Claus would not forget.

When she woke up Christmas morning it was terribly cold. Nobody had gotten up yet to make a fire but she wasn't going to let a thing like that keep her from getting out of her fold-away bed to see what Santa Claus had left under the tiny tree.

First, she reached for the doll. It had stiff legs and a very smooth head. Gently, Sarah turned it over. It didn't say "mama." And it didn't have on a pretty dress or shoes like the doll she had asked him for. How could he have forgotten again? She had even written him a letter in her class at school and told him again just what kind of a doll it was that she wanted. She had drawn a picture of the doll and colored her dress to make sure that he knew exactly which one to set aside for her.

She looked at her other gifts: a coloring book, crayons, a pencil box, socks, a bag of hard candy, and a funny-book.

There was no buggy either, the blue buggy that she had so wanted for her doll. Santa Claus had forgotten the buggy, too, just as he had done last Christmas.

Dolefully, Sarah looked into the next room. Her mother was buried beneath a mound of covers, snoring loudly. Her father was slumped down in a chair, sleeping and still wearing his overcoat and hat. His mouth hung open and an empty liquor bottle was on the floor beside him. The room smelled unpleasant, the way it always did when they had bottles of whiskey and stuff like that. Instinctively, Sarah turned up her nose, and she went back to the living room to get into bed again.

She hugged her doll in her arms. It wasn't the doll she wanted but it was a doll and it was new and it was her's. She hugged it tenderly and tears rolled over the bridge of her nose as she pictured the beautiful doll in the pink dress with the blue buggy.

Her mother had told her that he might forget again. She said that Santa Claus had so many little children to take care of that he sometimes forgot or made mistakes. That was why such bad kids sometimes got the nicest toys for Christmas. Not that they deserved them, just that Santa Claus made mistakes.

It was still snowing outside and Sarah could tell that it was very early in the morning because it felt like it was very early. She could hear a streetcar as it moved down the tracks.

Sarah wondered if her mother had ironed her dress so that she could go to the church across the tracks in the village and she also wondered if, hopefully looking toward next Christmas, there wasn't something she could do to improve Santa Claus' memory.

SONORA McKELLER, fifty-three years young, was born in Los Angeles and has spent nearly all of her busy life in Watts. One of the coordinators of the Watts Summer Festival, she is a triple-threat personality, who, as a community action worker for the Westminster Neighborhood Association, is said to have knocked on every door from one end of Watts to the other; an actress who has played leading roles in Harry Dolan's *Losers Weepers* and Jimmie Sherman's *Ballad from Watts;* and one of the earliest members of the Watts Writers' Workshop, joining when it was still a small, informal gathering in the Watts Happening Coffee House in the months after the revolt of 1965. She was given a powerful drive toward accomplishment by her father, a landscape gardener and Baptist minister, who every night would say to his six daughters, "I want to know what and if you're learning." After two years at Pomona Junior College, Miss McKeller became a nurse, then a singer and dancer. She worked in troop service for the Southern Pacific Railroad during World War II. She has studied at the U.S.C. School of Public Administration and has a certificate of leadership from the League of Women Voters. She is a familiar and vivid speaker at anti-poverty meetings. Part Negro, part Mexican, part Apache Indian, part German, she seems to have acquired both the fighting and the artistic qualities of all those peoples.

Watts—Little Rome

I was born in the city of Los Angeles in the year 1913 and have spent practically all of my life here. I believe it was the year 1929 when I first visited Watts. At that time, Watts was all-but-barren land. Houses were few and far between. Japanese produce gardens were everywhere. Where today we see storm drains and cemented gullies, in those days the people of Watts fished for crawfish and catfish in mud and slime . . . in fact the section was known as Mudtown. Watts boasted one movie house, a few schools, many Chinese lottery dens where one could play such games as blackjack, chuck-a-luck, four-five-six poker, and Chinese lottery — drawings every hour on the hour. The only nightspots were honky-tonks. They were really speakeasies — bootleg whiskey, gin, and home brew. In each spot a lone piano played by a local boy provided the entertainment.

Years passed. The depression came with its E.R.A., W.P.A., and other projects aimed at relieving the poverty-stricken areas. At the same time came the repeal of Prohibition, the eighteenth amendment — legal alcohol and an increase of alcoholics. Barreled "green wine" took its toll. Mental and physical deterioration was visible everywhere. Once healthy, hard-working family men became derelict "winos." Many died as a direct result of this "devil wine." Too late, the govenment stopped the sale of barreled wine.

During these years the city and county of Los Angeles reaped a bountiful harvest through graft and corruption. Twice our city's police chiefs and mayors were indicted along with the city's top underworld figures.

With World War II came a shipyard boom, airplane factories, and many new avenues of employment; and with it came the draft, the evacuation of the Japanese, and the influx from the South. Those were the years when Watts began to grow. The pioneers gave way to the migrators. Some moved into the West Side while others moved into Watts.

Pioneer merchants also moved to Watts. Safeway, Giant Food Markets, Karl and Kirby Shoe Stores, pawnshops, and haberdashers

— even Chinese and barbecue eateries — came to Watts. All came to prey on the people of Watts.

Even today, grocers charge, for certain products, three times as much as stores outside the Watts area. For instance, pinto beans can be bought for five cents a pound at supermarkets away from Watts, while here they cost from fifteen to eighteen cents a pound. Dress shops and clothing stores sell merchandise at three and four dollars above the prices in stores in outlying areas. A plain seersucker dress sells for six to eight dollars in Watts, whereas in Washington Park or at Manchester and Broadway the same dress sells for two dollars and ninety-eight cents. I know, because it is part of my job as a community action worker to check comparative prices. I could go on with more of these swindles. Suffice it to say that the people of Watts are fully aware of this situation. But what are they to do? With the transportation system being so poor, they find themselves trapped to buy in their own backyard.

The pawnbrokers follow suit, charging higher rates of interest than in any other part of the city.

For years Watts has survived virtually as a police state. Long before August 13, 1965, the police department has shown its strength in brutality. Nothing has been altered by the present city administration. Police officers continue to harass Negro and Mexican citizens. We, the citizens of Watts, have tried in many ways to find a solution that would eliminate this condition, but so far have run into nothing but barriers.

We are far from having a police "protector." Instead, men run and actually hide when a prowl car passes. A police car stops any citizen on the street and subjects him to public ridicule. "Stand over against the wall, place your hands over your head, and don't move." Then that is followed by a head to toe search of the person. "Remain in this position" while one officer calls the local police station to run the "make." If you are found to have even a jaywalking ticket, out come the handcuffs and off you go to jail. If nothing is found, out comes the record book, down goes your name, age, height, weight, color of skin, hair, eyes. Your public interview ends with, "You are clean this time, see that you remain that way. Remember we have all the facts on you." Often added is, "If you should find out from your friends anything that would interest us, give us a ring." That's how they dress up the word "stool pigeon" before sending you on your way. It's also how you are given an open invitation to get even with your "friends" by false accusations.

Lurid accounts of sexual sadism that sound like invented horror stories are, in fact, part of the sad facts of life in Watts. Over the years, you hear these stories too often to discount them as "stories." A woman is walking home alone after dark. The patrolmen pull their car up to the curb, get out, and flash a light in the woman's face. She is asked to walk a certain distance and told that she is under the influence of either narcotics or alcohol and that she is to get into the car to be taken to jail. She is next driven to a secluded spot, assaulted, and beaten. You may ask why the victims don't file official complaints — well, it's their word against yours, baby. The cop-out is too easy: her lover or her husband did it!

The school system in Watts is notoriously substandard. Many teachers who can't get jobs in other areas are assigned here. Often their main interest is not in the children's education, but rather in their own graduation to better schools in more prosperous sections of the city. Educational material is scanty, so the boys end up with few books and many sports. Where will they go after the drills, football, and all the games are over? Men cannot build a ship, a plane, or even a TV set with footballs and baseball bats. Most girls study home economics and social studies. Can't they learn to cook, iron, sew, wash, and budget in their homes? Where will they get credits to enter universities or colleges? How will these young men and women acquire the right kind of education they so badly need to fit them for their future?

As to the housing problems of our area — the public housing projects are overcrowded and overpriced, but the privately owned houses are often worse. Private landowners rent rat-, roach-, and termite-infested homes — poor structures at best; houses as old as Watts with plumbing of the same vintage, and electrical fixtures and wiring so fragile that they are virtual firetraps. Still, people need places to live and some crave privacy, so although these houses continue to deteriorate, the rents climb higher. Long before the Watts revolt, Watts was one of the most wretched cities in the world and one of the unhealthiest. Rats as large as cats and healthier than children would run in and out of the houses as if they were house pets. Vacant lots and condemned houses littered with garbage, tin cans, and other debris are interwoven with the densely populated community — such a situation can well create epidemics.

Should an epidemic of any form break out here, the people would die surer than a field of grain after an invasion of locusts. Watts boasts one small public health clinic, no receiving hospital, no emergency hospital, and few doctors. Many times in the past when emergency ambulances have been called, because they must come from places like Harbor or LA County General Hospital, or other places far away from Watts, an injured person has died while waiting. We have yet to see something done to correct this tragic situation.

Watts has been for years a more or less isolated city, though densely populated. People were accustomed to asking for little and getting less. Monotony had been their lot. Until the August 13, 1965, revolt, no one entertained a thought that Watts would ever undergo any drastic changes. Now everything has changed.

Whether the revolt was right or wrong, the way the city, state, and government officials conducted themselves after the revolt ended has left a large lump in the throats of American Negroes. The sight of city police officers standing by in battle array, watching people break and enter, loot and burn buildings without interfering or citing one person, watching with enjoyment as if it were a circus. Then the invasion of the National Guards and barricades, destruction of private property, needless but legal murders. These things leave scars. Illegal searches and seizures, breaking into private homes, brutal beatings, false arrests and charges, outrageous amounts for bail, point-blank refusal of jailers to give the "innocent 'til proven guilty" prisoners their right to communicate with relatives or friends within the time specified by law. To this very day, many who may well be innocent are serving time in various jails and prison camps. This will long remain in the hearts and memories of the Negro people.

Let us face facts. We Americans know the history of the founding of this America — continual warfare against the true American, the Indian. How many years did the white man bleed the Indian? How many years did the Indian bleed the white man? All this bloodshed was in the name of a peaceful America with liberty and justice for all. Since the first white man set foot on American soil, there has been nothing but war and bloodshed. War with Spain . . . war with England . . . even war with fellow-Americans . . . Rebels and Yankees . . . wars between states . . . wars against government. Is there any wonder that the American Negro should at last act in accord with the Great White Chief who fathered him? "Like father like son," they say. Can we not say of our August thirteenth revolt: "Blood will tell"? As our forefathers tried to establish peace with the Indians by quiet means only to resort later to war and still later to isolate themselves from the Indian by placing them on reservations, so have the Negro sons of America tried — since the time of brutal kidnappings and enslavements, enchainments and sales at the auction blocks — to live in peace with their white brothers.

We, the American minority, have slaved to enrich this America, have shed needless blood and lived in fear for the lives of our people — have gone to the battlefields to keep the enemies of this great country away from its shores only to find that when the enemy is vanquished we are returned to the position of nobodies, freed from visible chains but still bound by chains of prejudice. Who is the American Negro if he is classified as nobody until somebody needs him to battle for a freedom and safety he is denied? Who are we if nobody cares?

Now we are faced with the problem of digging out of the rubble. Where do we go from here? Will we at last become actual participants — active and recognized — in the overall pattern of social living? Will the city and the government help us to help ourselves? While America stretches forth its arms to the four corners of the world, embracing all nations in its bosom in times of distress, we the American Negro are slowly but surely becoming an individual nation. Today, as a wide-awake people, a people no longer gullible enough to swallow the promises of our white brothers — as we did in the past — action seems the only answer for us.

There is but little time to reach our goal. Freedom, equality, justice. Things that are rightfully ours, given us by God and the Constitution of our native land. We shall beg no more. Neither shall we ask. We shall demand. We have tilled the fields, planted the cotton and the corn, tended the cattle, slopped the hogs, nursed and mothered the young, laid the foundation for the wealth of this country, fought in every war to preserve that wealth and protect the freedom of the land. Now we demand the right to live in freedom and peace, rich in the knowledge that we will henceforth and forever be recognized, not as inferior Negroes but as free Americans.

I leave you now, dear reader, with this simple prayer:

Oh, Lord! My strength in ages past;
Hear my humble plea, shine down Thy light;
Show me the right way. Guide my footsteps in the way
Thou wouldst have me go.
Give strength, oh Lord! Add broadness to my shoulders,

That I might better be able to lend support to my faltering brother.
Let me not, Lord, be a shameful one in Thy sight.
Help me, oh Lord, to be proud of my heritage.
Let me never forget that all men are my brothers,
That I am my brother's keeper; Nor let me doubt that You alone
Created us one and all, and that You and You alone made all things good
In this land, for man to enjoy equally.
Not for color or creed; but because we are all Your children.
Lord! Open the eyes of the people of this our land.
Make them to see the errors of their ways.
Let them, oh Lord, amend their ways.

As in the days of Moses, I cry unto Thee,
Oh! Almighty God! Tell them to "Let Thy people go."
Bring back and instill in the memory of our government, Dear God,
The fall of Rome in the days of Nero.
Wake the people, Oh, Lord!
For you have placed in our hands
A weapon of desires for freedom, justice, and equality.
Help us, Dear Lord, to use these weapons for right and right alone.
Preserve the future of this great land.
Oh, God! Let us not, as Nero, fiddle while our country burns!

HARLEY MIMS was born on a farm near Indianola, Mississippi, in December, 1925. Three years later his family moved to town, where he attended school. He joined the Marines in 1944 and served for 23 months as a machine-gunner in the Pacific. After the war his deepest desire was to go on to college — eventually he was accepted at Brigham Young University in Provo, Utah. There he was the only Negro among five thousand students, and in fact the only Negro in the whole city. When Harley Mims returned to his family in the South, he tried to get a job as a teacher. Resented by the "Negro power group" for not having attended a small local college, he took a job as a porter until the principal of a nearby school offered him a position. He taught for two years, then moved to California, where he has lived ever since. He joined the Writers' Workshop early in 1966, and is now studying dramatic writing at the University of Southern California. Presented here are two sections from his novel-in-progress, entitled *Memoirs of a Shoeshine Boy*.

Memoirs of a Shoeshine Boy

1. Passing

You know what? If I could have my say-so about who my best buddies should be I still think I'd choose old Charley Washington, in spite of all the stupidity he has such a firm grip on. Oh, I know you can choose a lot of your own buddies and all, but when a guy's plowed right next to you and watered his mule at the creek next to where you water yours and lived all his life in the next house down the road, that feller is your buddy whether you like it or not. I liked it, really. But, honest to goodness, Charley's brought more bladder failures on me than I can shake a stick at.

Here's one example:

There was a white family in our hometown named Washington, same as Charley's family. They even had a boy named Charley too. Well, this here white Charley used to meet me and my buddy Charley on the street and pretend that he talked the same funny way he said me and Charley talked. Sometimes he'd have his daddy along with him and they'd have a hell of a laugh trying to mock Charley. Me and Charley would laugh right along with 'em, but when they went on their way we would call 'em all kinds of sons-of-bitches and such.

Then one day me and Charley went over to the next little old town about thirty miles away. And of all things, we ran smack dab into white Charley. He teased us a little bit before he went on about his business.

"Come on, nigger buddy," my pal Charley said to me; "we're going down to one of these fine hotels and pass for white."

I damned near pissed on myself right there. "Just how in the hell are two ebony-hued, liver-lipped bastards like us gonna do it — tell ourselves ghost stories until we turn pale with fright and then run up to one of these white cafes? And suppose our real color comes back to us while we're drinking our coffee? What happens then?"

"Nothing like that, old nigger buddy."

"Will you please stop calling me your nigger buddy? We're colored folks!"

Charley looked at me real cold-like. "Don't you dare call me a nigger," he said, making his voice sound just like the white Charley Washington. "You're my daddy's nigger yard-boy and don't you gimme no sass. Now shut up and come in."

Like a stark, raving fool I followed that idiot. We went straight to one of the finest hotels in the town and Charley went straight up to the desk and asked for a room.

The clerk gripped the edge of the desk and closed his eyes real tight. He opened his left eye real slow-like and looked at us again, then closed it back and shuddered.

"Oh no!" he moaned. "Not a hotel! You niggers done had every kind of *in* there is. Sit-ins! Wade-ins! School-in! And now a hotel-in! Oh, no! Please! Just go away!"

"You call me a nigger just one more time," Charley said boldly, "and my daddy will come in here and kick your ass!"

My bladder damned near failed me right then and there, but I tightened my legs and held on.

The clerk opened both eyes like he'd been goosed. "You're colored, aren't you?"

"Hell no!" Charley bellowed. "My daddy's yard-boy here is colored and he's a fine lad too."

I tightened my legs some more.

The clerk clutched his chest like one of them old-time actors in a silent film. "Oh, Lord, a liver-lipped white man! Chee!" And he stood there getting whiter and whiter. I guess me and him both were like two ghosts with bloodshot eyes.

"Will you please hurry up and have the bellboy show us a room?" Charley asked.

The clerk got a hold on himself then. His look got real dirty as he leaned across the desk to glare at Charley. "Prove you're white, sir." He straightened up and wagged his head and laughed. "Oh, not that I doubt you, sir, but so damned many foreigners come in here wanting rooms that we just have to check everybody."

"How dare you!" Charley said roughly, and grabbed up the desk phone before the clerk could stop him. Several white men in the lobby rushed over to grab Charley, but the clerk stopped them.

"No! No! Wait! He's white. He's gonna prove it."

The men let Charley alone and looked at me.

"I'm his nigger yard-boy," I explained fast as hell, then I peed on myself.

"I'm gonna call my daddy," Charley told the clerk. Then he asked the operator to get white Mr. Washington's plantation near our hometown. The operator got the number.

Charley on the phone: "Daddy? Me. Charley. . . . Look, Daddy, I'm over here trying to get a hotel room, but the clerk keeps calling me a nigger. . . . Okay, Daddy. . . . Aw right." Then he gave the receiver to the clerk. "He wants to talk to you."

The clerk was still smiling and looking all around when he took the phone and put it to his ear, but his expression changed right away.

". . . Yes sir. . . . Ha ha ha. . . . Yes sir, Mr. Washington. . . . Oh, no sir, Mr. Washington. . . . I see. . . . I'll send his bill straight to your plantation, sir. Now, really, sir, there's no reason for you to come over here and kick my ass. We were only teasing your son, but he got angry and called you. . . . Yes sir, I *do* remember that time you came in here with those pilots and tipped me twenty dollars, now that you mention it. . . . On behalf of the hotel, sir, I offer full apologies."

My bladder acted up again.

The clerk put the receiver down and looked at us like he was sick or something. He rang for the bellboy, gave him a key and pointed feebly toward us. "Show Mr. Washington and his nigger yard-boy to room fourteen."

"I ain't showing these niggers nothing!" the bellboy shouted.

The clerk pointed to Charley. "He's white! And you mind your manners!"

The bellboy took the key and politely asked Charley to follow him. He just rolled his eyes at me, but I followed him too. Hell, I had to. My bowels had to move real bad.

"He might be white," the clerk said to one of the men who had come over to pound Charley, "but if I was his daddy I'd sure keep my eyes on them nigger house-boys. I really would."

2. *Maggie*

"Well, tonight we'll take it out on Maggie," he grinned.

"Ain't that the truth," I said. "Now let's shoot pool. I can't stay down here all day."

Maggie wasn't a bad-looking girl. Well, she wasn't pretty either. Oh, I don't know exactly how to describe her sometimes, except that she didn't look so much like a damned mule as some of the other girls in my hometown. Oh, I ain't saying that everything's all wrong with me and Charley's girl friends to make fun of and all, but some are so ugly that you just have to feel sorry for them sometimes. I kinda believe that a whole lot of hard work makes a woman ugly. Of course, you will see a lot of rich girls too ugly to cry, but a rich girl, when she's ugly, looks a little different from poor, hard-working, ugly girls. At least they look a little different to me. But Maggie *was* different. Now, she might be ugly as all hell to a total stranger, but I guess I've looked at her so long and so much that whatever ugliness is there has sorta mellowed down to where I don't notice it too much. But sometimes Charley thought she was beautiful.

That night when we went by her house she was still eating supper, her and her widowed mama.

"Y'all come on in and have supper, boys," her mama called out. "We got fried rabbits and collards."

"Nome," I said, "but I thank you, Mrs. Lizzie."

"I'd eat if you had some chittlings," Charley said. "We have chittlings at our house tonight, so I'll save my eating for home."

"It's the wrong time of the year for your daddy to be killing hogs." Mrs. Lizzie forked a piece of rabbit off the platter and offered it to Charley. He took it. "Of course, if your daddy done stole somebody else's pig he'd have to kill it off fore he got caught, wouldn't he?"

We laughed some at that. She was always teasing old Charley about something or other. I kinda thought she wanted Charley to marry Maggie — from the way she carried on and all.

"Maggie cooked that rabbit, Charley," she went on. "She said you boys might stop by to see her, so she sorta fixed it up specially for you. Course, we'd a had chittlings too if we had a man around the house to go out and steal somebody's pig for us. But us poor women have to do the best we can."

Charley quit chewing to look at her. "Maggie's big enough to catch pigs," he said. "And you got that old pistol in there under the mattress which you can blow its brains out with yourself."

"We don't need no lesson in hog stealing, Charley Washington," Maggie piped up. She had rabbit grease all around her mouth. "Have another piece of meat and wait for me out on the gallery."

"I'll do just that," Charley said, and reached over and got his second piece of rabbit before either of them could lift a fork. Then me and him went out on the front porch to wait.

"Shore is a good night for chasing coons," Charley commented, looking up at the big, round, yellow moon that seemed almost close enough to touch. He chumped on the rabbit a few minutes before he said anything else. "Old Spot don't care much about night hunting no more. He just likes rabbits mostly."

"I saw that dog of yours try to rape a coon once," I reminded him. "Remember? The coon raped him."

"Yeah, buddy. I remember. Old Spot ain't been the same since. He gets real shame-faced when he sees a coon now. But he still has a ball raping rabbits whenever I turn him out."

"Honest, Charley, you ought to not keep Spot fastened up from girl dogs like that all the time. He ain't got no sex life at all. He probably wishes he was dead or something."

"He ain't so bad off." Charley tossed the cleaned rabbit bone into the yard and wiped his hands on his pants leg. "He's doing all right on that rabbit stuff. Just them boy rabbits give him hell about being screwed."

I let it drop. My mind went back to Mr. Hokum and Jo-Jo and that key. Right now they just might be in the barbershop's rest room taking the flooring up to get started on the tunnel digging. I felt cold for a minute. What would happen if the police caught them going in or coming out? Would they tell where they'd gotten the key? They might forget and leave some of them floor boards up where Mr. Lotus would find them in the morning! I tried to get over being scared by thinking of all that money we'd get from the robbery. I tried to think of Maggie.

Maggie came out of the house with a piece of rabbit in each hand and sat down on the edge of the porch near us. If her and Charley ever got married, I thought, they really would have a hell of a grocery bill. She could eat almost as much as Charley any day at any meal.

"Y'all ain't been to see me since last week," she began. "How come?"

"We been working hard," Charley lied.

"I thought maybe the preacher been throwing bricks at you two again."

"Where'd you hear something like that?" I asked. Right now it looked to me like we might as well button our flies and go home because we wus out of luck. "Folks shore do lie on me and Charley."

"Preacher told Mama he chunked y'all away from his house about his daughter."

Charley acted real mad then, like his feelings had been hurt real bad. "That preacher shore can tell lies. We don't want that old skinny daughter of his. Yeah, we had a light argument — but it wasn't about no daughter of his. He called Wilbur a fat-lipped bastard about two dollars he owed us for hauling some hay outta his field. He just don't want folks to know he don't pay his debts, that's all."

Maggie acted like she believed it and all because she just laughed and let it drop. She finished the two pieces of rabbit and threw the bones in the yard. Then we got to telling jokes and laughing until we heard Mrs. Lizzie go to bed.

"How long is it gonna take her to go to sleep?" Charley whispered to Maggie. "I ain't gonna sit here all night telling jokes. I got chittlings waiting for me at home."

"It won't take long," Maggie said. "She didn't drink any coffee at suppertime and coffee is the only thing that keeps her awake."

"Well, she'd better start snoring soon or I'm going home," Charley grumbled. One thing about old Charley; he'd say right out loud how he felt about things if he wanted you to know.

Maggie got up and strolled out into the yard where the moonlight touched her like a soft veil. She stopped and looked back at us kinda like them women do in the movies when they want the hero-boyfriend to rush out and grab 'em and hug 'em and everything. Charley took his pants off and went on out into the yard where she was waiting. He didn't hug her or anything like that; he just said a few words and both of them laid down right there. I got ashamed and looked the other way. I heard a lot of sniggling, then everything got real quiet except for the crickets and bull frogs and katydids out in the bayou. About us was the soft night and there on the hard, unyielding earth a man and a woman were into that one act no living animal flesh could deny or ignore except in misery and anguish and fright, and even then only because staying alive and safe was more important. I tried not to think of them. Tomorrow I would laugh with Charley about it all and I'd tell him of the times me and Maggie had sneaked off to the cotton house. Hell, she was supposed to be Charley's girl but he didn't care none about what I told him because he said he wouldn't marry her nohow. He said if he couldn't trust her now he could never trust her as a wife. You see, me and him loved girls but we'd sorta made a bind between us not to fight over one no matter what happened, because if either of us ever found a girl we'd really want to marry the other would not violate nor attempt to violate her apparent honor and faithfulness. Me and him just had to put our backs together in some corners to survive the onslaught of heaven-knows-what.

The cabin door opened suddenly behind me and Mrs. Lizzie was on the porch with a lit lantern and a double-barreled shotgun.

"The shotgun is for you if you try to run," she told me. She put the lantern down and reached just inside the doorway and got a whole bundle of prepared switches — heavy ones like the ones mules' asses are whipped with. "These are for Charley for messing around with that preacher's daughter. He oughta know by now that he belongs to my Maggie." She started down the steps. "Get that lantern and come on out here."

"Yes'm," I said.

Why in the hell don't Charley get up and run, I thought as we moved toward him and Maggie. He couldn't have been that engrossed in what he was doing not to have heard us or seen the lantern. Then, when the lantern's yellow circle of light crawled over them I saw why he hadn't made a break for the woods.

Sure, Maggie had let him get on top of her and everything, but she'd entwined her legs around his legs and her arms around his arms so that he couldn't move. Now, Charley had real hard, tight muscles in his butt and these muscles had made his behind gather up in a knot. He wasn't wiggling for pleasure or anything like that. He told me later that he'd been trying to break her entwined grip every since he'd laid down because the first thing she'd told him after she got him where he couldn't move was that Mrs. Lizzie was going to take the hide off his rear end about tom-catting around with the preacher's daughter.

Mrs. Lizzie told me to stand on the other side of them and hold the lantern high enough for her to read her target well. I did. Charley's butt looked sorta pitiful all tightened up like that. Mrs. Lizzie laid the shotgun down in the dirt and pulled a long willow switch out of the bundle. She cut the air several times and the switch made a swishing noise: s-w-i-s-h! s-w-i-s-h! s-w-i-s-h!

"Now, Charley," she began; "I reckon you won't go chasing after other girls when my Maggie is here cooking rabbit and waiting for you. Charley, I love you like I would my own son, so, like my own son, I figure you sorta need chastising."

She raised her switch arm high over her head, carried it all the way back and raised one foot high in the air like a baseball pitcher. I shuddered. She held the pose like a real professional for a moment, then brought the switch snapping through the air like an evil snake.

Ka-pow!

Charley let out a yelp.

The arm went up again. Slow. The foot rose for balance. Slow. The switch cut through the air.

Ka-pow!

Charley tried to wrestle himself free. Mrs. Lizzie threw three more fast whacks across his rump and he started crying.

Maggie pulled her head away from his face. "Charley Washington, don't you get no snot in my hair!"

"Damn your hair!" Charley shot back. "I'll get snot in your face!"

Mrs. Lizzie put three fast, hard whacks in on him. He wiggled real fast. I thought he was trying to go on with his lovemaking, but he told me later that all thoughts of sex had fled his mind — that when he wiggled like that he was trying to shift the muscles in his tail so that she wouldn't strike the same place twice.

When he settled down again she cut him two real slow blows. He yowled.

Mrs. Lizzie looked over at me. "Hold that lantern close. See if I raised any welts yet."

"Yes'm." I held the lantern down real close to Charley's rump. I got too close.

"Thanks a whole lot for burning my ass with that lantern, old buddy," Charley moaned. "Thanks a heap!"

"I'm sorry, Charley."

"Well, how's it looking?" Mrs. Lizzie snapped.

"Kinda rough and ashy," I said. "Maggie, you shore know how to hold a man down, don't you?"

"I been practicing."

"Y'all intend to beat Charley to death and make me watch it?"

"A little chastising ain't ever kilt a healthy boy like Charley," Mrs. Lizzie said.

I stood up again with the lantern. "You shore ain't doing his piles no good, though."

Mrs. Lizzie got a new switch from the bundle. "He ain't got any. He's used corn cobs for toilet paper so long he probably grows shucks in his hip pockets."

She ka-powed down on him about six more times, then quit. "Now see if you can't keep away from that preacher's daughter and stay true to my Maggie, you hear?"

"Indeed I do," Charley said. "True till I die — and that ain't no lie. Maggie is the only one I'll ever look at again as long as I live."

"You can let that rascal up now, baby."

Maggie untwined.

Me and Charley started for home right away. He didn't even put his pants on. He rolled them up and carried them under one arm.

"That was a big promise, old buddy," I said as soon as we got away from the house. "If you keep your word you can't ever even touch a cow again."

"Like hell I can't," he said. "You know what a big liar I am. Now let's get on to my house before the chittlings get cold."

One thing I can say for old Charley: you might crack the bark on his ass a dozen ways to Sunday, but you can't kill his appetite.

"Okay, old buddy," I said.

But the chittlings hadn't got cold. As a matter of fact Charley's folks had just sat down to supper when we got there. We stopped in the yard long enough for him to put his britches on again, then went on into the house.

"Have some supper, Wilbur."

"No, thank you, Mr. Washington," I said. "I'll wait out on the front porch till you get through, Charley."

"Then how about some chesternuts?" Mrs. Washington asked me.

"Yes'm. I thank you."

"Well, go on and have a seat and I'll fetch 'em out."

I went out and sat down on the front porch and a few minutes later she brought me a saucer full of meat and a fork. I ate it because I didn't want to be impolite. I reckon she forgot about the chestnuts because she never said anything else about them.

Finally, Charley got through eating and came out and I whispered to him about the chestnuts his ma had promised me.

"You had it already, you fool," he grinned. "She didn't say chestnuts. She said *chester*nuts. We castrated our old hog Chester today and she just served it to you on that saucer."

I'd never be able to look that stupid hog in the face again, I thought.

LEUMAS SIRRAH was one of the original handful of young writers who responded to Mr. Schulberg's efforts to establish a Writers' Workshop in Watts in the fall of 1965. He has always wanted to become a chemical engineer, as well as a writer and artist. Leumas was born in Los Angeles in August, 1947. He did very well in school until the twelfth grade, when, at the age of sixteen, living by himself, he had to drop out and get a job to support himself. He began to write when he went to the Westminster Neighborhood Association and joined Schulberg's classes there. Several of his poems have since been published in *Los Angeles Magazine, Time,* and *Scholastic*. He and his mascot, a black cat named "Thought," have been residents of Douglass House since its inception. He hopes to have another chance to go on to college.

Infinite

Never know a begin of me
  Death God give to me
Never know an end of me
  Life God take from me
Never know proof of infinite
  Time God save for me
Always know of me
  Heaven and Hell infinite.

Me — I'm Black

I'm black
I'm black
I can't change the fact
Understanding I don't lack
I'm me — I'm black.

I'm me
I'm me
I can't change that
Today is black
Tomorrow, yesterday
I wasn't promised.
I am what I am —
That's all that I am
I'm me I am
I'm black
I'm black.

You and I

You and I know
You and I think
In between
You and I need
Past, present, future.
You laugh, I laugh.

You and I experience
You and I feel
Opportunity
You and I seek
Simple, compound, complex.
You cry, I cry.

You and I understand
You and I learn
Black with white
You and I lack
Birth, life, death.
You fight, I fight.

Who's Life?

Love is part of
Who's life? If a
Part of loneness is —

Woman is part of
Who's life? If a
Part of man is —

Night is part of
Who's life? If a
Part of day is —

Birth is part of
Who's life? If a
Part of death is —

Man is part of
Who's life? If a
Part of life is —

God, Infinite.

One, Two, Three

It takes two —
night and day —
To make one complete
cycle: God is past, present, future.

It takes two —
right and wrong —
To make one complete
struggle: God is work, play, determination.

It takes two —
male and female —
To make one complete
child: God is individual, radical, mankind.

It takes two —
land and water —
To make one complete
earth: God is sun, planet, moon.

It takes two —
good and bad —
To make one complete
belief: God is birth, life, death.

It takes two —
black and white —
To make one complete
man: God is simple, compound, complex.

But —
It takes three —
people
To make one complete
God: God is Infinite . . . A process, an effect
and a change causing — A process
an effect
a change . . .

Insanity, the Question

Higher, higher as can be the happiness found
as high as can be.
Happiness can't be found in height alone;
Tell me what you see.
Ask me of all to what I see the happiness as:
Cool, calm and free. To me the question is:
Ask as high as I am.
The happiness you do not share, yet it's high
And free.
Yes high, higher and higher than high but it is
Not up to me to give, to share the happiness,
Though free but to you.
Happiness higher than I, cool, calm and free.
Why do these thoughts I try to find?
Higher, you asked to see, would be impossible.
The thought of happiness is not here. For that
I speak about is the why question. And
Height. For yes, height to make the question difficult
You know, for that height is Insanity!

Who's the Man Asleep?

I.

. . . I am wondering could life be saved for mankind . . .
I've been asleep — a long sleep but now I've awakened.

I must let you know — now — that I didn't know of
my sleep. Life to me was wonderful

for I knew what I knew as Reality —
Not knowing I was the man walking along sleep.
Yes, I of all people seeking — to help — individuals,
races — but most important was the desire to help —
humanity.
I went day to day
Lived as any other person.

I saw, felt, and heard others but they were awake
while I was asleep. Going back in my past, I can remember
first, the thought of the problem. I felt it was not
the way people lived
but the way they thought.

So I thought it was their thinking —
Because of my walking in a sleep I knew nothing about.
Second, I felt that — maybe — drawing my friends
to the idea of Unity, to one point of thinking
would be something —
To begin a new way of thought, to set a way of life
that could start improvement by — mental communication —
to establish some kind of understanding,
knowledge, logic, emotion, and belief
in the problem of living.
I thought this might be something.

It was because of my sudden awakening to Extra Sensory Perception
and my sudden discovery of reaching others.
So I thought.
— This awakening was only a move in my sleep of walking —
Tomorrow, Yesterday, Today, practice! Practice concentration,
deep concentration — listen to the air currents
while listening to conscience, day after day,
not knowing if what I mentally hear is true or not —
Surprise. Success — the words, the very words I beamed out —
You can hear me, I know you can hear me —
The very words I heard — Ooh, I hear you, I hear you!

Being the person asleep while walking
I only turned on my back, only woke for a moment

And from nowhere as I entered,
I tried to spread, to develop this to be used
to help one another — and to encourage many.
I actually woke up when I found the Los Angeles County Jail my
home.

II.

Now I remember the thoughts as a child — coming to my head while I slept at night — "You're Samuel Harris number 12, you're Samuel Harris number 12" — over and over very dim, very dense but nevertheless I heard it
STOP
The man asleep, walking with the others has come awake — as I entered the jail for days and nights of torture. Yes, it was here that I found out that I was — or had been — asleep. For here what was said mentally was never said verbally and this I called — *untalkable facts*
STOP
Being the person asleep (in this state I found out) made it impossible for me to be heard by others, which made me different. So it was taught to others — To this day this is the only reason I have for the harm they tried to bestow on me — The first night forced into — No, it started with one or two words, then any word possible was forced into my mind. I found out that someone else could hear this word, no matter where they were, could pick my level of thought — "You're Samuel Harris number 12, Samuel Harris number 12" — that voice, my brain — bouncing as if on a rollercoaster — I hear it again, I hear it again, You're Samuel Harris number 12, Samuel Harris number 12"
STOP
I awoke to the darkness of the light, me the man that knew no begin of me — This number, what, why, where, when, who is it for? — The meaning puzzles — No, it didn't puzzle me, for every word forced into my mind made me realize things I knew I didn't know I knew — The number, ah yes the number was a name, for a certain level of thought — I must use it for identification purposes — for probation officers, police officers to identify the one who was reaching outside of the jail — or for many other reasons
STOP
There's much more, more, but I must find out, yes, in every detail — Being asleep now I'd like to go back but I know what I know — as I

look over my shoulder — for as I've said these are supposed to be Untalkable Facts — But would I accept the fact — and not, yes not try to consider myself crazy or insane — For if *you* would, could, should . . .
STOP
Think again for me to be that man asleep and wake up as I did — I accept what I've awakened to, as well as I accept the fact that I was born to be crazy or insane — Yet I am still — *Existence* — Yes, I am wondering could life be saved for mankind? — Life I thought I knew; life I never knew; life on another plane, yes, level of — *thought* — The question, Who's?

BIRDELL CHEW, the ninth of fourteen children, was born in June, 1913, in the flag-stop town of Mumford, Texas. Her father, a farmer, died when Birdell was nine years old, and the family then moved to College Station, Texas. There her mother took the first of various low-paid jobs. Birdell was never able to attend school for long, and sometimes the family went hungry. During a serious illness, which started when she was twelve and lasted several years, she began writing poems and stories. She was married at nineteen, but the marriage was not a happy one and eventually she and her husband were divorced. Ill health continued to prevent her from working enough to fully support herself or to attend school, but she read, and taught herself assiduously. She was also able to do voluntary community work, for which she has won considerable recognition. She was one of the earliest members of the Watts Writers' Workshop, joining it while meetings were still being held at the Westminster Neighborhood Association immediately following the revolt of 1965. "The Promise of Strangers" is the first chapter of her novel-in-progress bearing the same title.

A Black Mother's Plea

Please do not put a limitation on my son's possibility, because his skin is black. Allow him a free chance to make mistakes while he searches for himself, same as you do the Whites.

Please do not deny my son a job that he can master, because his skin is black. Allow him a chance to earn the money to build the tower on his castle, as high as he is capable, same as you do the Whites.

Please do not pick my son up off the street and beat him into admitting he committed a crime that he didn't do, because his skin is black. Allow him a fair chance in court to establish his innocence, or prove him guilty, same as you do the Whites.

Please do not shoot my son in the back for wanting to vote, because his skin is black. Allow him a chance to assume his responsibility, same as you do the Whites.

Please do not give my son a reason to hate, so he will destroy himself while he is still a boy. Allow him a chance to fill his heart with love for all mankind, for he was conceived by woman from man, same as the Whites.

The Promise of Strangers

1.

When I awoke early one May morning the sun was shining brightly, heating the whole shack as it flowed through the open door and cracks. I stumbled to my feet from a quilt I slept on in a corner of the living-room floor, which also served as my parents' bedroom. Rubbing my eyes to get the sleep out, I went to the kitchen and ate the corn-meal mush that was left there for me. This was my breakfast, for as long as I could remember.

After I finished eating, I went outside to look for my brother Frank and sister Callie. They were older than I, but still too young to chop cotton. I went up the road looking for them, not finding them till I came to a run-down unpainted shack much like ours. A little girl sat on the ground crying. I went into the yard and sat beside her.

That was the first time I remember seeing Sue. I patted her on the shoulder, saying, "Please don't cry, baby." But of course she didn't answer because she was only nine months old.

Every day after that, if it wasn't raining too hard for our families to be in the field, I would walk up the road to her house, and each time I found her crying I'd do funny tricks like standing on my head, rolling over like a dog, or hopping around on one foot until she stopped crying and began to laugh.

It wasn't long after I began to play with her that she was able to walk well enough to follow me around and soon she learned to jabber a few words. We played on the edge of the swamp at first, but by the time we were two and three, we began roaming through the swamp freely. In a year's time we knew it as well as the wild animals, and were nearly as wild as they.

Sue and I were the youngest of each of our families, so we didn't have to begin working in the fields as early as the other children and went completely unnoticed longer than any of the others.

Because we were too young to work we went and came at will. Our parents didn't seem to care, as we weren't of any use to them right then.

They were uneducated Louisiana share-crop swamp farmers who

worked themselves and their children, little more than babies, from sunup to sundown. We grew poorer each day, if that was possible. Both of our parents looked like old people, and had always seemed old to me. Neither of them ever had the time or strength to pay attention to how they looked, nor did they seem to care.

There were thirteen children in Sue's family and fifteen in mine. But by the time she was four years old and I five, most of our older sisters and brothers had either run away from home, or were married and living in the same kind of poverty. None of them were trying to make a better life for themselves. They found it easier to blame the white people for all their hard luck. The ones that were still home hung around getting their tongues worked out trying to raise cotton in ground that wasn't fit for growing, until they were twelve or thirteen. Then they ran off too. All but my sister Callie, who died when she was six years old.

Sue and I still did nothing all day but wander, getting into everything we could. The first time we went deep enough into the swamp to get lost, I knew we were and was afraid, but tried to keep Sue from knowing. She felt something because tears gathered in her eyes as she said, "Me tired, Johnnie, and scared too."

"Don't cry, Sue. Me take care of you. We rest. Then me take you home to your house."

"You ain't scared?"

"No, ain't nothing to be scared for."

Her tears began to dry, and she looked at me with pride. "You big boy — hey Johnnie?"

"Yes. And be bigger tomorrow."

"Me be big too?"

"A little, but me be great bigger."

I found our way out, feeling like a man because I had kept my promise to her. This meant a lot to me because I wanted her to believe that I could and always would take care of her. We had grown so fond of each other that nothing could keep us apart, not even measles.

That is how we grew up, roaming the swamp, ragged and dirty, clinging together. Taking a bath on Saturday night and putting on half-clean clothes on Sunday — never any shoes. Our parents didn't think that children of our age needed them. Each day we grew wilder, like the weeds. By the time I was six I was tall as an eight-year-old, with dark skin, straight nose, and thick chopped-off curly hair. Sue was tall for her age too, with light brown skin, dark brown eyes, and long golden-brown hair. Anyone could tell she would grow into a beautiful woman, for even then her prettiness outshone her ragged clothes and dirty face.

Growing up in the swamp offered us many advantages. We learned all about the small animals in their natural state — birds, rabbits, squirrels. We saw how they were born, how they ate, and how they lived — what they were really like, not as people write about them. And we learned what wild foods to eat, ourselves, by watching them.

One day while following a rabbit, we chased it deeper into the swamp than we had ever gone. We came upon a beautiful wide grassy space with a little brown house on it and children playing in the yard. They were having a lot of fun. We sat at the edge of the wood, out of sight, watching them until a pretty young woman came to the door and rang a bell for them to come inside.

We remained very still after they had gone inside. It was shocking to us to see such a young girl with so many children. We just couldn't understand it. Although there were a lot of children in our families, our parents were old. She was young, and she had more children than we had ever seen all in one place, unless it was at church. We knew that wasn't a church because it didn't have a cross on top of it. There was a big flag on a tall pole in the front yard, only we didn't know what it was then because we had never seen a flag before.

Sue looked wishfully at the little brown house trimmed in bright yellow. "Me want a pretty house like that, and a lot of pretty children like her."

Looking at her sweet face and sad eyes made me want very much to make her happy. I said, trying to make my voice grown up, "Someday me will buy you a house like that."

"You will, Johnnie?"

"Yes."

"When?"

"When us get married."

"Us going to marry?"

"Yes."

"When?"

"When me is tall like papa."

Her eyes lit up, making me feel much taller than Dad and more man than he could ever be. For I knew even at this age, that Dad was beaten by life. He had neither the courage nor the strength to fight against the unjust way he was letting himself be forced to live.

2.

Each day after we found that little house, we returned to our hiding place and watched the children play. And seeing them so happy, we grew happy, hopeful and bold. We didn't realize what we were really longing for until a few weeks later. All we knew was that we wanted to have fun, to play on their slides and swings and to play games with them. But we were too shy to join them, so we watched from our hiding place.

One day we became so enchanted by their gay laughter that before we realized we had left our hiding place, we found ourselves in the middle of the yard surrounded by happy children. We became frightened and tried to run, but each time we tried to break through or crawl under their hand-link ring they blocked our way. If we attempted to climb over, they shook us back into the ring. This went on for quite a while, us crying and they laughing. Then two of the bigger boys caught and held us, telling us not to be afraid, that they weren't going to hurt us. But we yelled and kicked as if we were being beaten.

The pretty girl who always rang the bell came out to see what was going on. When she saw us, she broke through their ring and stopped in front of the boys who were holding us, looking shocked to see such ragged, dirty little children.

We stopped fighting and stood there shaking like scared trapped rabbits. Big tears ran down Sue's cheeks, making long dirty streaks. That was the first time I knew her face was dirty. It made me so ashamed that I lost my fear, fought myself free and tried to grab Sue from the boy who held her.

The teacher took hold of my arm firmly, but kindly and said, "Hello." I stared at her but didn't speak. She asked my name and I still said nothing. Then she said, "Don't be afraid, no one will hurt you." She knelt in front of Sue and wiped her dirty face with a pretty white handkerchief. "Hush, honey, don't cry — I am not going to hurt you. Please don't cry. Now now, that's better. What's your name?" Sue was too afraid to speak but she gave a shy smile. The lady stood up and put the dirty handkerchief back in her pocket, then turned back to me and said, "Please tell me your name." I was still too frightened to tell her. "Did you come to enroll in school?" she asked.

We couldn't answer. Besides being fearful, we did not know what she was talking about, because neither of us had ever heard the word "school" before.

Sue looked wishfully at her and said, "Me want to go in your pretty house."

"That's fine. Have you ever been to school?"

"No m'am, me ain't got no pretty schoolhouse like you all."

"Where do you live?" she asked.

I answered her then, pointing toward the swamp. "Over yonder through the woods."

She smiled as if she thought she had won our confidence and we would stay to answer more questions. But we were still afraid. She told the boy who held Sue to let her go, and we took off soon as Sue was free. The boys took off after us, but the teacher stopped them.

We ran till we were deep in the woods, then sat on the ground to rest. Sue said, "What is school?"

"Oh — me guess that's the name of her house, like Mr. Frank's house. That big one on the hill."

"Do you want to go in her house?"

"It's pretty."

"Let's go tomorrow."

"If you want to."

After we rested, we went home, walking slowly and very quietly, wondering "What is school, what is it like, what do they do when they go inside? I want to go." I would ask Mama, but she had never seen it, so she wouldn't know either. I looked at Sue and wished her mama would comb her hair and put her on a pretty dress like the other girls had on so she could look pretty too.

That evening when I went to the pond to get water for the hogs, I washed my face for the first time that was not a Saturday when I took a bath. And the next morning when I went for Sue I took a rag with me. We stopped at the pond and washed her face and hands, and I picked some of the straw out of her hair.

When we reached the schoolhouse, the children were inside. We sneaked up close and sat on the ground under an open window. When they recited their lesson, we tried to repeat after them. But we didn't understand the meaning of what they said, and we didn't even know what two and two *was,* so we couldn't follow them very well.

Sue got some dirt on her arm and I washed it off again, saying to myself, "When me get to be a big man, me going to buy her a gang of dresses — prettier than all of them."

The bell rang for recess and we crawled under the house and watched them play till they went back inside. Then we ran into the woods.

We lay under the schoolhouse every day after that on Sunday. No one was there on Saturday so we played on the swings and slide as we had dreamed of doing. This was the first real fun we'd ever had.

Our mothers took us to church on Sunday morning. I don't know what for because none of us enjoyed ourselves. We sat in the back, listening to Father O'Brien say words that meant nothing to us. We couldn't understand them and I'm sure our mothers couldn't either. We gained nothing by going, and our mothers acted the same lifeless way going back home as they acted while going there. They talked very little to each other and said nothing to any of us. So they weren't helped either.

Our dads never went to church, and each Sunday when we returned home my dad would be walking through the shack grumbling about how mean Mr. Frank was, and blaming him for all "his" lack of courage. When he had worked himself into a rage he would begin to shout at Mom and pretty soon my mind could take no more of his carrying on. I'd flee to Sue's house to get her, because I knew her dad would be doing the same thing. Then we would sneak into the swamp, crying and wishing we could go to the little schoolhouse right away, but we knew it was too late to get there and back before dark. So we clung together till the burden of not understanding our dads' frustration rested a little lighter on our shoulders. Anyhow we knew they always fell asleep after they'd stopped raging.

We were too young to know that they were drunk but we knew something had to be awfully wrong to make them carry on like they did each weekend. All other days they were quiet, with blank-looking faces, and didn't seem to know there was a Mr. Frank, or care.

None of our sisters or brothers walked back home with us when we came from church. They were old enough to know what was wrong with our dads, so they stayed in the little town. Neither of our moms seemed to care that they weren't with us, and they didn't ever say anything unless one was missing when they were called to go to the field the next morning. When that happened, our moms would cry for a short time and our dads would grumble — saying how they worked themselves to death for a bunch of lazy, no-good kids. Then they would forget. Most times the one that was missing never returned.

Sue and I were too small to escape, so we continued sneaking to the schoolhouse and watching the children play — our mental escape. We did this till we were caught by some big boys. They carried us inside, kicking and fighting like wildcats, and took us up to the front of the room where Miss Robert sat. Then they stood against the door so we couldn't get out.

We stayed there in front of her desk, barefoot, ragged, and mud-caked, shaking like we had the rickey. Sue was crying, and I was trying hard not to.

The children laughed at us till Miss Robert asked them kindly but firmly to be quiet. Then she asked us in the same firm voice to tell her our names. After we did, she said we should sit on a seat near her and listen to the other children recite their lessons. When it was time for recess and the others went out, she closed the door and asked us a lot of questions about ourselves and our parents. We told her as much as we could about ourselves, but nothing of our parents for we knew nothing to tell. We didn't even know our parents' names — or our surnames. We had never heard anyone call them by their names. Mom called dad "Pappy," and he called her "Mama," and Sue's parents called each other that, too. Us children called them "Mom" and "Dad."

I know it sounded foolish to Miss Robert, but she asked no more questions about them right then. She asked us again if we wanted to attend school.

"Yes m'am," I said.

"Ask your parents to let you come tomorrow."

"We don't have to," I said.

"No. Me go where me want," said Sue.

Miss Robert patted her head. "Well, ask them anyway and if they say you can come, you be here early tomorrow morning." Then she told us to go home.

We left the school grounds but we didn't go home because no one would have been there. Instead we played in the woods out of sight and watched the children until school ended for the day.

We had never asked our parents if we could do anything. So we did with that as we did with everything else. We wanted to go to school — so we went.

3.

The next day we started school. Sue was five and I was six. We went three days wearing the same dirty clothes before Miss Robert guessed that we hadn't asked our parents — but she didn't say anything to us.

When we left school that evening two of the bigger kids followed us far enough to see where we lived. Later that evening, Miss Robert came to see my parents.

When Mom opened the door and I saw who it was I crawled under the bed to keep Miss Robert from seeing me. I was ashamed of Mom's dirty clothes and our house. And most of all I hated Miss Robert to tell her our secret. Sue and I wanted to keep our first and only happiness just for ourselves, and I thought if she didn't see me she wouldn't know I lived there. Then there would be no need for her to tell.

I felt glad when she asked Mom did she have any school-age children. I thought it meant she didn't know I lived there and that our secret was safe.

Mom said in a flat dead tone, "Yes. But I ain't going to let 'em waste time tryin' to be like white folk — what good that do 'em?"

Miss Robert tried to point out all the advantages we could have with an education that we wouldn't have without one. But Mom still said "No."

Then Miss Robert asked if there were any other families living near us who had school-age children. Mom told her the Silveras had some, but there was no need to bother them because they felt the same as she did about school.

Miss Robert didn't go to Sue's house. I guess she felt Sue's parents wouldn't give their permission for her to go either. But she did accomplish one thing: she learned our and our parents' whole names.

When Dad came home, Mom told him what Miss Robert said, and asked if I could go to school.

He said if I went to school I would want things the white people would never let me have and then I would get into all kinds of trouble because that was all book-learning ever did for Negroes. He went on and on, telling her about the Negroes he had heard of who had gotten into trouble. Not knowing if the people were educated or anything else, all he knew or cared about was that they were killed by white people. "I don't have time to hide in the woods to keep from being killed just because that fool child want to act like white folks."

Mom said, "I guess so."

That was the first and last time I ever heard either of them talk about school. Education was something they honestly thought would do Negroes more harm than good. And they knew we already had more of the bad things in life than we needed, so why look for more?

But in spite of their saying no, Sue and I went right back the next day, just as dirty as ever. Miss Robert never asked us if our parents said we could come. She washed us, combed our hair, and gave us clean clothes and shoes to wear at school. We changed back to our dirty clothes and took off our shoes each evening before we went home. But if it had not been for fear of getting them dirty we could have kept them on, because no one paid enough attention to us to know what we had on.

Even though Dad had said I couldn't go to school, he did not care enough about me to find out whether I obeyed him, and neither did Sue's dad.

We were so eager to learn that in a few weeks we knew almost as much as the other children our age. And we got along with them just fine, because after the teacher cleaned us up they accepted us as one of them.

When I turned eight years old, I had to go to work in the field, but by then I had learned enough to study alone, so I could sneak out and study in the field. In the evening after I quit work, Sue and I would go to Miss Robert's house and recite my lesson. When Sue had to go to work, she did the same thing. On Saturday and Sunday afternoons she gave us tests and our grades were always very good. During the rainy and cold season we attended day classes and went to her house at night to study.

Miss Robert and her mother taught us all summer. We went in the daytime, while we waited for the cotton to open enough for picking. When it was ready, we went at night. Her parents looked after us as if we were their own children, and she treated us like we were her sister and brother. Before we met them no one ever had time to care what happened to us. Now we learned that we were human beings not wild animals and that even if our clothes were ragged we should keep them clean and take a bath every day. We wished we were their children so we could live at their house instead of in our rundown shacks because at home it was so difficult for us to do all the things they taught us to do. We had hardly any clothes except the ones that they bought for us and we had to leave them there. Our own ones we had at home were just rags, and our moms hardly ever washed them. We had to sneak to take baths unless it was Saturday.

So Sue and I took our baths in the pond during the summer and in the barn when it was cold. I watched for her while she took hers and she did the same for me.

We finished the little country school when Sue was ten years old and I was eleven. It only took us through the seventh grade but Mrs. Robert, who was a retired teacher, taught all the children who couldn't go to school in town and wanted to study further.

By that time all of our sisters and brothers had left home. Our dads had almost stopped trying to raise crops. They mostly sat in the fields and drank. And our moms sat quietly looking hopeless and deader than ever. Of course Sue and I didn't care if they did not plant cotton. It wouldn't grow, so there was no need for them to have ever planted any. And it gave us more time to study. We knew by then that education was the basis on which we should begin trying to build a better life.

We talked a lot about how hard it was going to be for us to finish our education, and we wondered if we should run away like our sisters and brothers. But we hated to leave the Roberts, so we tried to raise enough food to feed ourselves and our parents and we studied very hard. We knew that we wanted very much to finish high school and that we would, no matter what we had to endure.

One evening while we walked home from school Sue said, "I'm going to be a grammar-school teacher. I've thought about it a lot, and I could do it well."

"I want to be a doctor." I began to think of it when my sister Callie died. I didn't know then what type of doctor it was who took care of children, but I knew I was going to be that kind when I got grown.

"Where will we get the money, Johnnie, to go to college?" she said, looking thoughtful though not discouraged.

"Miss Robert said we can find jobs and work our way through college."

"What will we do about our parents? I know they won't ever move away from here."

"I don't know, Sue. When the time comes, if our dads won't go, I guess the only thing we can do is take our mothers with us and leave our dads here."

We remained quiet for a while, then Sue said, "You know something? When I was a little girl, I used to look at my parents, and they seemed so old to me that I wondered if they had ever been young. Sometimes now I wonder the same thing."

"I do too."

I guess Dad was about forty-eight but he looked and acted like an old, old man. I doubt if Mom was forty-five but she looked almost as old as Dad. Sue's parents looked just as worn-out as mine. They were always ragged and we had never seen our dads take a bath or heard them say they were going to.

Each time I looked at my parents I felt sick inside. I wondered how Dad thought he could be any worse off with an education than he was without one. Many times I wanted to ask him to let me read some of those papers Mr. Frank was having him sign. But I didn't want him to know I could read because then he would have known I was going to school and this would have made him afraid for our safety. So I let him be and hoped I could prove to him some day how wrong he was.

4.

Sue's birthday is in January, and on the day of her thirteenth she was very proud to be in her teens, same as all girls — really growing up. We went to the Roberts' house early that evening and they surprised her with a birthday cake. The first one she had ever had.

We sang Happy Birthday to her and that was the first time I'd seen her cry since she was a little girl.

It was very cold when we left their house, but our happiness was too deep for us to feel it. Sue's party had given me as much joy as it had given her. It was the first birthday cake I had ever seen too. Neither of us had eaten any kind of cake but a few times before, and then only at the Roberts'. They not only gave us our first taste of cake, they gave us the only decent food we had ever eaten. Before we knew them, we didn't know people cooked any food except black-eyed peas, rice, beans, potatoes, corn bread, and cornmeal mush.

When we came in sight of Sue's house, we saw that it was on fire and began running toward it. We came close, hidden in the high weeds that surrounded it, and saw a gang of sheet-covered men, standing around watching it burn.

Sue made a move to run toward it again but I pulled her back into the tall weeds before anyone saw her. We crawled far enough away to take a chance on running, hoping we could make it to my house, but before we got there we saw it light up in a quick gasoline-like blast. We lay on the ground, hidden by tall weeds, shivering and waiting for the white sheets to leave. It wasn't until our house caved in and was almost completely burned up that they left, laughing and shouting as if they had had a wonderful time. We crept close to the burnt house and stared in shock at two black heaps lying among the red ashes.

We fled back to Sue's house, hoping her parents had gotten out and were hiding someplace, waiting for her. But when we got there we found what was left of her dad's burnt body hanging from a tree in their backyard. The remains of her mother's body were lying in the dead ashes of their house.

Sue screamed and we ran into the swamp and didn't stop till we reached the Roberts' home. I banged on the door frantically until Mr. Robert opened it. Then I pushed Sue inside and fell in behind her. She stood on the spot where I pushed her, shaking with her mouth open as if she was hollering, but no sound came out. And I was trembling with such deep anger that when they asked what was wrong, I could only yell, "They burned up our parents!" over and over again, till someone slapped my face.

Mr. Robert shouted, "Who burned your parents, John? When? What for?"

But by then my mind had gone blank as Sue's, and I could say nothing. Someone led me to a cot in the living room and put Sue on the couch.

A long time later, I heard her crying softly in a heartbreaking, scared way. I went over and sat on the floor beside her, and so did Miss and Mrs. Robert. They were crying too and I was still fighting mad. Mr. Robert had gone to see if he could find out what had happened to our parents.

The bright January moon was hidden behind black angry clouds by the time I could talk, and rain was hitting on top of the house so steadily it sounded as if a river was flowing over it.

We sat in the dark a long time, listening to the rain pour down. Mrs. Robert whispered, "John, do you feel like trying to tell me what you saw? And do you have any idea who killed your parents, or why anyone would do a thing like that to them?"

"I don't know who killed them, Mrs. Robert, or why. I wish with all my being I did know." Anger closed my throat again. I couldn't talk about what we had seen and it was many years later before I could.

I was boiling with anger and would have killed whoever had done such an evil, crazy thing if I'd had a chance. Not out of love for my parents, but because I wanted to punish their murderers. It was such a cruel, animal-like thing for men who thought of themselves as human beings to do to harmless and helpless old people.

Mr. Robert came back a little before daylight and said that he and four other men had gone to our houses and found out that what we had seen wasn't just a bad dream. A man who lived on Mr. Frank's farm told them that Dad and Mr. Silvera had butchered two of their own hogs without asking Mr. Frank, and that was why they had been killed.

Mrs. Robert asked why they had to get permission to kill their own pigs and he told her that everything people raised on share-crop farms belonged partly to the landowner, who had to get his part first. Most times they would take everything that was fit to eat or sell.

Miss Robert said, "But surely that's not fair, Dad."

"I know, honey, but that's the way of sharecroppers. I can't see why people keep killing themselves and their children on poor farms like that. If they want to be swamp farmers, they should buy a few acres and raise sugarcane. Then they wouldn't have to ask for what was rightfully theirs."

A man named Sam Moss told him and the other men that Mr. Frank had gone to our houses earlier in the day, made a big fuss, and threatened our dads, who both ran into their houses and locked the door. Mr. Moss left and a gang of sheet-covered cowards passed his house after dark on their way out to our farm. He hid behind his barn until they had passed, then ran through the woods to warn our dads, but by the the time he reached the Silveras' house, the mob had it surrounded. He couldn't warn my dad because he couldn't get to our house without passing that mob, and he was afraid to try. He saw them beat Sue's dad with a whip till he dropped to the ground. Then they hung him to a tree, threw gasoline on him, and struck a lit match to him. After that they set fire to his house. They must have killed Sue's mom first, because she didn't try to get out or scream while the house was burning. And he was too afraid to go and see if she was in there after they left, so he just ran home.

"I guess they knew your parents were in their house, John, so they didn't bother to drag them out — they just set fire to it," he said angrily.

What Mr. Robert told us was so shocking that none of us could speak when he had finished. He too seemed to have run out of words, and we all sat quietly, staring into the fireplace till late in the morning.

For three days no one came to the Roberts' house, and no one left it but him, and he carried his pistol each time.

Miss Robert closed the school for a week, because she knew it would take a few days for the people to get over their fright.

Sue and I sat on the couch all day and late into the night, holding hands and staring into space. We might have talked to each other and maybe to the Roberts, but I don't remember.

Eight days later, Father O'Brien came to speak to Mr. Robert about what he could do legally with Sue and me. Mr. Robert was a farmer and also a lawyer. He and Father O'Brien knew there was nothing that they or anyone else could do or would try to do about what had been done to our parents, but maybe they could do something for us.

We were asked a lot of questions about our sisters and brothers. My brother Richard was the only one I knew how to contact, and Sue knew where two of her sisters lived, but they were married to swamp share-crop farmers and had a house full of children they couldn't support.

Miss Robert felt it was safe to start school again after a week passed, but Sue and I didn't return. We didn't feel like going, we were still too confused.

Father O'Brien came back a few days later, had another talk with Mr. Robert, and then Mr. and Mrs. Robert talked quietly to each other. She later asked us if we thought we would like to live in New Orleans.

We looked at each other, and Sue's eyes lit up with shock and fear, tears filling them. She looked as if she was just realizing that her parents were really gone and she was all alone. I held her hand tightly to remind her that she still had me to take care of her. Her tears began to fall, and I pressed her hand with both of mine. "Please don't cry. I'm here with you."

I turned to Mrs. Robert. "If we go to New Orleans, will we live in the same house?" I asked.

"I don't think so, John."

"Then we would rather stay, Mrs. Robert."

"We'll see what we can do, John."

Then she asked Sue how she felt about it.

"I want to be with Johnnie," she tearfully said.

"You don't have to decide right now. Why don't you go for a walk and talk together," she said.

We walked in the woods, back of their house, walking and thinking till we were deep in the woods. When we came to a big log we sat on it and, as I looked at her pretty, sad, tear-stained face, I knew I didn't ever want her to be very far from me. I felt I had a right to take care of her — it was my place to do so. I was only fourteen, but I knew I could and would work to support her if there were no other way for us to be together.

"Sue, do you want to go to New Orleans?"

"No. If it means we can't be together like we have always been, then I'm not going no matter what anyone says. If I let them separate us, who will see after you? No, Johnnie, we'll stay with the Roberts."

"I don't think we can, Sue. I heard Mr. Robert tell Father O'Brien that he'd like us to stay with them and we could help on the farm for our keep. But Father O'Brien said that if we stayed, Mr. Frank might make trouble for them, so it was best for us to leave."

"No, Johnnie!"

"That's what he said."

"Maybe Mrs. Robert can find us a place close together, where we can live and work till we finish high school. Then the only time we will be separated will be when we go to college."

"That would be good! It would be no different from the way we have lived all our lives, and I could still see after you."

We were very young, but we were no longer children. We knew we belonged together and we would find a way to keep anyone or anything from separating us.

When we returned to the house, Sue's sisters and my brother were there. Her sisters were glad to see her and to know she was alive. They thought she'd been burned up in the house with their mother until Father O'Brien told them differently. They offered to give her a place to live, but said she couldn't continue in school.

Miss Robert told them it was better for them to let Father O'Brien find her a place to live where she could both work and go to school.

They agreed, because they wanted her to have a better chance in life than they had. If she lived with them, they couldn't help her, for they had nothing with which to help themselves.

My brother didn't act glad to see me, but when asked what he could do to help he said he could get me a job working by the day on the farm where he worked.

Miss Robert asked him if I would have a chance to go to school. He looked as if she had struck him. "No!" he replied in an angry voice.

She told him that job wouldn't do. He said I was too big to waste my time fooling around a schoolhouse. What good would it do me?

They had a few more words. Then he left.

Father O'Brien came back two weeks later, and brought a man and a beautiful woman. They were my oldest sister and her husband. She had run away from home when she was twelve years old, before I was born. In the newspaper, she had read that Father O'Brien was looking for the children of Frank and Fannie DeFrance, who lived in a certain Louisiana swamp town. She called the telephone number that was listed, but he wouldn't tell her why he was looking for them till they came to see him. The same type of plea was in the paper for Sue's lost sisters and brothers, but none of them ever answered.

First they went out to our farm and after seeing what was left of the burned house, they went to find Father O'Brien. He told them all that had happened, and they came to the Roberts' to get us. I would live with them and Sue would live with their close friends.

Sue and I were grateful to them and I silently thanked God for answering our pleas.

It was sad parting with the Roberts, even though we all knew it was better for everyone. And certainly we would have a greater opportunity for education in New Orleans than we had had in our home country.

We would never forget the Roberts! They had shown us the only kindness we had received from anyone. They had taught us that we had a God-given right to try to prove our worth in this great world He created, and that education is the key to the door of success; we must have it to be capable of taking advantage of whatever opportunity came our way, so we could reach our goals in life.

Sue and I sat in the rear seat, holding hands and never letting go for one second unless it was a must. As the road carried us away from the little town I was born in, I had disturbingly mixed feelings — sadness, anger, hurt, gratitude. It had given me nothing but poverty and heartache, but even so I felt I was leaving a part of me there.

Sue sat quietly, most of the trip looking straight ahead. I knew she felt I had my sister to help me, but aside from me she had only the promise of strangers whom she had never met.

Appendix

THE TRIAL OF T.

Part I: Statement from T.

Leaving school one day, going southeast to Compton, I boarded a bus on Central Avenue at 103rd Street. I was going to take care of some legal business pertaining to the Selective Service System. As the door closed I saw my sister. "Hey, Marsha," I called, and waved my hand. I could hear her voice calling back to me as the bus took off.

While I was saying to myself, I'll go over there to visit her as soon as I get back, I was looking at all the old places that I had seen so many times before. It was familiar to me — I'd lived there seventeen years. The only sight out of the ordinary — a group of girls whose looks were so sweet that they sparked my eyes.

Buzz-zz. I had pulled the cord, to let the bus driver know I wanted to get off, at Rosecrans and Central. I snapped my finger, saying to myself, Goddam, Ring, Stop. It was too late. The bus continued. Oh, well, I said to myself, I'll get off at the next stop. I did and started walking until I got to Compton Boulevard.

Turning left to proceed east, I heard a familiar high-frequency sound. Yes, it was a siren about four hundred feet away. I quickened my steps to see what was going on. When I arrived, I saw a man being stopped for a ticket. Since I was working in the civil rights movement, I decided to stick around and watch the procedure.

Standing next to a nice-looking lady, later known to me as defendant R.'s wife, I said, "What is happening?" I was concerned. She said the police were stopping him for a ticket. "What for? Speeding?" "No, for not signing the ticket," she told me.

Mr. R. and the arresting officers began to get a little on the loud side, so I made sure I was out of the way: a good ten feet away. Defendant R. said, "I'm not going to sign that ticket." Some people stopped. The police called more policemen.

While R. was talking to the ticketing officer, another officer came from behind and grabbed R.'s arm and neck, choking and squeezing him. I asked for his badge number. Because, as I said, "That's the way riots get started." The officers pushed and shoved R., who was not resisting. I said, "We shall overcome this." I watched them brutally shove R. into the police car. R. was saying, "If you stop hurting me, I'll sign the ticket." The policemen said, "It's too late, goddammit," and pushed him onto the seat.

Suddenly, someone said to me, "Move, you dirty punk!" I looked up, saw it was a police officer, and asked myself, Is he crazy . . . ? I said to the officer, "No, this is public sidewalk." He said, "Move, you black punk," again. I wondered, Is this man out of his mind? I replied the second time, in a very polite way, "No, it's a public sidewalk, and I'm going to stay here if I want to." He called another officer over to us. I was standing there quietly and he said, "I told this dirty punk to move nicely, and he wouldn't move. Will you witness for me?" Then he said again, "Move, you dirty black punk."

I had gotten angry and was ready to fight, but I thought, The law is backing them. So I just stood there looking him angrily in the eyes. Because this time I said to myself, I've just got to go to jail. My mind was reacting very rapidly. I had already said, "I'll fight to the federal court if I have to."

I put my hands behind my back and let them arrest me. The officer pushed me into the car, slammed the door, and said, "Let's get the hell out of here." He got in the other side of the car, and the second officer got in the front and they headed for the Compton Police Department. They were later known to me as Officers J. and O.

Officer J. said, "You motherfucker, you think you are smart, don't you?" I felt a swift, fast, and hard chop to my intestines. "Answer me, you dirty punk," he insisted, striking me again. I still said nothing. He got very angry and said, "You motherfucking punk-ass bastard, you answer me!" He struck me a few more times. I was thinking, Should I laugh, or let the baby have his fun? "What's your name?" he asked, grabbing me by the neck. I finally gave in. I realized these bruises weren't doing me any good. "T.," I said. One of them said to me, "You wait until you get down to the station. We're going to kick your black ass. We're going to see how tough you are."

We drove up to the police station. They dragged me out of the car and started pushing me. I was pushed into a jail cell. "After you eat your dinner, I'm going to beat your ass." "I can't wait to see this!" said another police officer.

The booking procedure was not long for that particular station. He fingerprinted me on three sets of large filing cards. "Write your ABC's and your numbers one to nine." After completing that part of the procedure, I took my first mug shot, turning to the side and looking at the X on the wall. He then pointed to the west wall of the room. "Sign on the three lines that are marked with an X."

After signing my name, I was put under security. I looked around the small cell, and I saw an old dirty mattress, which was mine. I dreaded to lie on it. . . . It would have been easier to lie on the floor balled up like a squirrel. I woke up next morning with my chest all congested, my nose running, and my eyes watering. I was kept in the same cell for three days.

When I got out I called Mr. Schulberg, whose writing class I had been attending. I told him what had happened and asked if he would come to the court with me on the day I was to appear.

Part II: Statement from Budd Schulberg

Nineteen-year-old T., then enrolled in Westminster's Youth Training Program, was one of the early members of our Writers' Workshop. He called to say he had missed our last class session because he had been arrested. He was upset because he had had no previous police record, which in itself is something of a record for a young man growing up in the streets of Watts. He asked me if I would accompany him to the court in Compton.

We agreed to reach the court an hour before he was to plead so that there would be time to discuss the case with the public defender. We were both concerned that he might be railroaded because his case balanced on his word against the word of four police officers. We could not find the public defender until just before the case was to be called. He was a white man who seemed completely uninterested in T.'s problem. I told him I was interrupting my own work and devoting this entire day to T.'s case because I felt he was making a serious effort to advance his education at Westminster and in my class, and a conviction on this kind of a charge would seriously disrupt his young life. The public defender did not seem at all impressed by my intervention in the case. He obviously regarded me as one extra nuisance with which to cope. "Before you get too involved, take a look at what this boy has done!" he told me. He showed me the detailed police complaint. It accused T. of shouting the most extreme obscenities at the police and exhorting the crowd that had gathered to "get those white motherfucking cops — let's start the revolution now!"

"That is not necessarily what he did," I said. "That is only what the police *say* he did. Just because they're policemen doesn't make them any more reliable as witnesses than T. is. He swears he never said these things. He says the police built up that case to cover up their own unfair arrest and their beating him in the police car. I came with him because I wanted to see that he gets a proper defense."

The public defender shrugged and said, "I better get you somebody else."

He called over a Negro public defender in his middle thirties, Mr. P.D. He took us to a small office, studied the charges, and asked T. to tell him his version. He said he knew of my work as a writer and had heard of the Watts Writers' Workshop, and he thought it would be helpful to T.'s side of the case if I testified for him. But he said that even while he believed T.'s story, it was his duty to warn him that he saw little chance of getting an acquittal when there were four police officers lined up against him. He felt the wisest thing might be to have T. plead guilty to a lesser charge and then he would talk to the judge about suspending the sentence due to T.'s youth and efforts to improve himself despite having dropped out of high school.

"But it isn't fair," T. said. "I don't want to plead guilty, even to a lesser charge. I will swear I am innocent. I was just walking along and saw the police using what I thought was excessive force to make an arrest, and I asked the man for his badge number. After all I'm a citizen of this country. Don't I have the right to ask him for his badge number?"

"Theoretically, you do," our Public Defender said. "But sometimes you have to be practical in this world. I can't tell you how to plead. I can only advise you. Faced with this line-up of witnesses it's my duty to warn you that I think we'll lose the case if we plead not guilty."

It was at this sticky moment that a new element entered the case. The attorney for R., the other defendant, had located a witness, a white house-painter who had been working outside the radio store and standing close to T. at the time of his alleged "inciting to riot" and "obstructing arrest" and "resisting arrest," etc. This unexpected witness was in his mid-sixties, still wearing his paint-daubed overalls. And to improve matters, he was a retired deputy sheriff.

"Well, now I think maybe we've got a case," our P.D. said. "I'm still not sure we can win it against the police department. But there's a fighting chance."

The next decision was whether to let the judge hear the case himself, or to try it with a jury. Mr. R. preferred the judge because he was anxious to get back to his job as manager of a restaurant. But T. and I talked it over and decided to take our chances with a jury.

The case proceeded with all the solemnity and attention to detail of a major trial. It took half a day to fill the jury box. I was the first witness for T.'s defense. Under our P.D.'s questioning, I described T.'s faithful attendance at the writing class. I also tried to place his questioning of the police badge number in some perspective. T. was on the student council at Westminster and he had discussed in the writing class his plan to make a report on the police behavior in Watts that he felt provoked gathering crowds and incited the kind of spontaneous combustion that had set off the week-long uprising of August, 1965. He was also engaged in helping to form a Watts teen-age group called Youth Organization for Progress that would help to improve conditions for his peers in Watts. He and his associates believed that police brutality, one of the most pressing problems of Watts, could be lessened if the police were made to feel they were themselves under watchful and thoughtful observation. I said that although T.'s actions may seem provocative to an outsider, it might be understood if seen within the context of T.'s ideas and activities.

The cross-examination from the district attorney was unexpectedly severe. My credentials as a character witness were questioned on the grounds that I saw the defendant only at my class for a few hours once a week. I answered that our Workshop often went on for three or four hours and that writing is such a personal activity that one exposes himself far more through writing and discussing his work than one would in a math or science class. It seemed a strange platform from which to be discussing the Writers' Workshop but in Watts one becomes accustomed to the long arm of the police reaching through most unexpected windows.

Our P.D. felt that this testimony had strengthened T.'s case, especially when it was followed by that of the white house-painter, who insisted that he was within hearing distance of T. and had not heard any of the inflammatory statements T. was alleged to have hurled at the police in an effort to incite the crowd and prevent the arrest.

The three uniformed policemen and one plainclothes detective all repeated their charges against T. But Lieutenant J. did not seem to help his case when he testified that he had not struck the defendant in the police car or called him "Nigger," but that he had said, "You dirty little punk, where's your big mouth now?" and "It's dirty punks like you that give the rest of them a bad name." He and his fellow officers seemed to have no awareness of the fact that no matter what they thought, T. was innocent until proven guilty and they had no right to pass judgment on him in the police car or challenge or insult him.

The trial began on a Monday morning and was not concluded until Friday evening. Mrs. Schulberg and I attended every day of the trial and our secretary, Miss Sally Bowman, took down the entire courtroom proceedings in shorthand. The full text is too lengthy to include here but the entire cross-examination of T. is reproduced and the summation of the Public Defender. It should be noted that taking the case on the spur of the moment, Mr. P.D. provided a conscientious, shrewd, and finally eloquent defense of T. And throughout the week-long, hard-fought trial, The Honorable H. S. proved himself a judge of deep understanding and concern for fair play. Aside from the unheralded verdict rendered in this case, which will be found at the end of the transcript that follows, there was also an unexpected bonus as a result of this trial. It might literally be called "poetic justice." Judge S. found himself so interested in the Watts Writers' Workshop at Douglass House that he came to attend Workshop sessions and later became a member of our Board of Directors. As such he has been active in advising our writers as to their legal rights, helping them extricate themselves from pressing legal problems, and in one vital case using his good offices to recommend to fellow judges that some young men be paroled to Douglass House, where they could work and develop, rather than stagnate in the county jail.

Part III: In the Courtroom

Public Defender made opening statement: "Our case is very simple . . .

Defendant intends to show by his evidence that he came upon the scene, saw what appeared to be an unlawful arrest, asked for a badge number, when it was refused, retired from the scene. When the emergency came to end, was then asked to remove himself from the sidewalk in a derogatory manner. He refused to do so, as he had a legal right to be there. He would have removed himself though if he had been asked in a prudent manner.

T. sworn in.

Public Defender.

Q: What is your business occupation?
A: I am in school — Westminster — and high school at night.
Q: In connection with those duties do you counsel?
A: Yes, in my own age group.
Q: At approximately 8 P.M. in reference to events in this case, can you tell us what transpired.
A: . . . went to see what was going on, heard loud voices. I stood aside and one of the policemen seemed to be very belligerent.
Judge: You approached the scene, you heard loud voices. Tell us, tell the jury what the officer was doing, what Mr. and Mrs. R. were doing. You cannot say he was not acting right, or come to a conclusion.

Public Defender.
Q: After hearing loud voices, you approached the officer?
A: Yes, I did.
Q: Did you say anything to him?
A: I asked for his badge number. I saw one of the officers grab Mr. R. I said, "See, that's what makes these riots get started."
Q: Did you say it in the voice you are using now?
A: No (and he raised his voice to indicate how he said it).
Q: Where were you standing?
A: About twelve feet from the scene.
Q: Had persons gathered?
A: If they had gathered I didn't know because I was not facing them.
Q: After you made that statement, did you say anything else to the officer?
A: Yes, I said we shall overcome this. Someone was telling me I was some kind of nationalist — one of the officers said this to me.
Q: Prior to your making this statement, had Mr. R. been handcuffed?
A: No. The officer still had him around his neck and . . .
Q: Anything unusual in face of Mr. R.?
A: Yes, he looked as though he was about to choke.
Q: Why did you say this is how riots started?
A: Something I had seen in August seemed like a similar occasion.
Q: Who were you addressing this remark to?
A: To one of the officers.
Q: Did you say this to influence the crowd?
A: No, I was trying to get the officer to stop doing what might arouse a crowd into a negative attitude towards the police.

Q: In other words, you tried to get something across to the officer to avoid anything further happening. Had a crowd gathered?

A: A few high school students . . .

Q: Did you at any time turn your face in the direction of the crowd and admonish them from doing anything in reference to the officers?

A: No.

Q: Did you notice how many persons were in the crowd?

A: Approximately twenty to twenty-five.

Q: Teen-agers?

A: Yes, some, and some business people from establishments nearby.

Q: Was the crowd noisy?

A: No, it was not.

Q: Did you hear any profanity in the crowd?

A: No.

Q: Did you use any profanity?

A: No.

Q: Now you heard testimony of the officers, and you heard certain statements attributed to you. Did you make any of these statements?

A: No.

Q: Where were you standing when these police officers came to the scene?

A: When police officers [names] came to the scene I was standing approximately five feet from the police car and Officer J. said . . .

Q: Were you standing near anyone when Officer J. made these remarks?

A: No.

Q: What was the first thing Officer J. did when he came out of the car?

A: He came towards another officer and said something to him.

Q: Did you hear him order the crowd to disburse?

A: No. Not Officer J.

Q: Did you hear him say the crowd was an unlawful assembly?

A: No.

Q: Did he say anything to you?

A: Yes. "Move, you dirty punk."

Q: Did he ask anyone else to move?

A: No.

Q: When he said, "Move, dirty punk," where was Mr. R.?

A: He was already handcuffed and in the car.

Q: How many patrol cars were there?

A: Two, and four or five others arrived on the scene.

Q: In what kind of voice did Officer J. speak to you? Loud, moderate, or soft?

A: In a loud voice, "Move, you dirty punk." I said, "I am not moving."

Q: Was it any louder than that?

A: No. When he told me, "Move, you dirty punk!" I said, "I am not moving, this is a public sidewalk." Then he called another officer and said if I didn't move, I would be under arrest.

Q: Did you at any time walk between officers and Mr. and Mrs. R.?

A: No.

Q: How far was the closest person to you when you were under arrest?

A: Four or five feet.

Q: Did Officer J. come over and ask you to move after you attempted to get his badge number?

A: Yes.

Q: Did he give it to you?

A: No, he didn't.

Q: What was the first thing that happened after you were under arrest?

A: He put me in the car. When we were driving Officer J. started hitting me.

Q: What were you doing?

A: Nothing.

Q: Were you handcuffed?

A: Yes.

Q: Where were you sitting?

A: In the back of the car.

Q: Was it a light blow?

A: No, it wasn't exactly light.

Q: Did you have any discussion in the car?

A: He said I was the type that was bad for . . .

Q: I am asking this question because . . . I don't want you to misquote the officer and use your own words. Do you recall the specific words?

A: I don't recall specific words, couldn't quote exactly.

Q: From what you recall, what were his words?

Objection . . .

Q: As best you can recall, what did the officer say?

A: . . . your kind of Nigger that makes it bad for the good Negroes.

Q: He used Nigger and Negro?
A: Yes.
Q: Did you state anything prior to his making this remark?
A: No, I did not.
Q: What did you hope to accomplish by asking the officer for his badge number?
A: It goes back to more than that particular time . . . I had been doing quite a bit of research . . . I asked for his badge number because I thought it might put some fear in him.
Q: Did you have it in mind that in some way it could avoid an explosive occurrence?
A: Yes, I did.

District Attorney.
Q: Where were you coming from when you arrived on the scene?
A: From school.
Q: Where is school?
A: In Watts.
Q: Where is that?
A: . . . Westminster Neighborhood Association.
Q: Did you take a bus?
A: Yes.
Q: Where did you get off?
A: Rosecrans and Central.
Q: You walked, how many blocks?
A: I am not sure.
Q: As you were walking, did you meet any friends?
A: No, I didn't.
Q: How wide is the sidewalk at the radio shop?
A: I wasn't standing there.
Q: Well, where were you standing?
A: . . . six to eight feet.
Q: Did you notice that that sidewalk is unusually narrow?
A: No, they all seem the same to me.
Q: Could you tell the court and jury what you first noticed when you arrived in this place?
A: When I arrived . . . they were talking very loud . . . R. and the police officer.
Q: Will you describe the instance which preceded your asking for the police badge number?

A: Actually it was the way he was acting with the defendant.

Q: How long had you been standing there before you asked for his badge number?

A: Not very long.

Q: What did he do?

A: He was shouting.

Q: . . . outrageous?

A: I didn't say outrageous — I never heard a policeman talk in that loud a voice.

Q: How loud — shouting?

A: Yes — louder.

Q: Did you know the nature of the transaction between R. and police officer?

A: By that time, yes.

Q: So before the officer started to place arms around his neck, you were watching this scene so closely you didn't notice a crowd gathering?

A: I would have had to turn around to see, and I was watching R. and the officer.

Q: You testified at some time you saw twenty or twenty-five people. At what point?

A: About twenty seconds after the officer had placed his arms around defendant's neck.

Q: Is that when you made your statements?

A: I said, "We shall overcome this."

Q: And you were unaware of other pedestrians?

A: Yes, of those behind me.

Q: Did the crowd get larger than twenty to twenty-five?

A: Yes, forty or forty-five.

Q: Did you make any statements to the officers after Mr. R. was handcuffed?

A: No.

Q: You didn't hear any announcement for the crowd to disburse?

A: No, I wasn't interested in the crowd.

Q: Did you ever turn around and make any statements to the crowd?

A: No. I directed my statements to the officer that his actions were what started riots.

Q: In the meantime an officer stepped out of his vehicle and went directly to you?

A: Yes.

Q: And just the two of you there until Officer ——— came? How many times did he tell you to move?

A: Three times.

Q: Then when he returned with another officer, how many times?

A: Once.

Q: And did you move?

A: No, I didn't.

Q: Are you concerned about rioting?

A: Yes.

Q: At this time you were going to demand your rights to stand on the sidewalk. Didn't you think this might influence the situation?

A: No, I didn't, it was just between me and the officer.

Q: And you weren't concerned about your arrest?

A: Yes, I would think twice before doing this again, but he came to me and talked to me like I was a junkie or something, and I had to stand my ground.

Part IV: Public Defender's Summation

I will try to make my remarks as brief as possible. You've heard two sides. Instead of arguing, I would like to reason. I believe firmly that our system is the greatest in the world . . . I believe that the law as it stands is color-blind. It always has been . . . in reams of evidence we can lose sight of the essential issue . . . not so much who said it, but what was said. It is not a case of T. against the police, or the police against T. — it may be a Madison Avenue expression, but there is a credibility gap here . . . if we believe everything we have heard here . . . does this mean that one or the other must be a liar? I don't think so . . . sometimes we fill in . . . and we think something happened that didn't happen . . . by the time it gets to the other end of the table it is completely emasculated. This is a principle of the human mind . . . the power of suggestion.

Officers came upon the scene . . . there was an arrest . . . persons gathered. From evidence it was a rather quiet crowd. Neither one of the officers admitted they were threatened by the crowd, but there must have been excitement. Someone comes along this scene, carrying books . . . hears sound of loud voices, observes out of curiosity . . . voices loud. Something in the officer made T. pause, observe the scene, then ask the officer for his badge number. You did recall officer said he was engaged in a struggle with R., but was still able to watch the mouth of T. verbalizing. There is reasonable doubt that he could do this. There must have been some sound. The rest he filled in with his imagination, remembering what happened last August . . . and this youngster had the audacity to ask him for his badge number. There are indications of his not being sure of himself and he might have been afraid when he was asked for his badge number. T. did not approach the cars . . . simply asked for his badge number . . . he was a youngster. Why didn't the officer arrest him for disturbing the peace? He didn't. He ordered him to move. He was simply standing there. When officer said, "Move, you punk," he refused to move. He was then arrested. The witness, a house painter standing beside him, heard no profanity. T. submitted to arrest. The officer in the car initiated a conversation with, "Where is your big mouth now?" Officer J. admitted that the crowd did disburse when he asked them to. The defendant was standing alone on the sidewalk. Inspector ——— said he was trying to inflame the crowd. Would you ask a man to join the crowd he was trying to inflame? He is nineteen years old, in many ways immature, attempting to play the role of a good Samaritan, now being accused of disturbing the peace. He was asked many times to move. Why would you ask him many times? Defendant refused because of the manner in which he was requested. I believe he had a legal right to stand his ground . . . dignity and right of the individual . . . an officer as an agent of the state is not free to implant the idea of crime in the mind of an individual . . . but to prevent it. If he was disturbing the peace, he should have been arrested.

How can he obstruct the arrest? It implies that by not leaving, public interest was threatened. A similar argument was made before the Supreme Court in 1956 arising out of the incident in Little Rock. School officials had to deprive Negro litigants' right to attend a school. In order to keep the peace, they deprived them of their rights. R. and his wife were already in the car, the crowd had dispersed, where was T. to go? It is clear the officers were angry, defendants were angry, and there was poor judgment on the part of all concerned.

We had some character reference from Mr. Schulberg. Young T. was known to be peaceful, honest. One thing came out in his testimony, T. has taken an interest in counsel with others, very interested in averting occurrences in the street. That is why he asked officer for his badge number. In T.'s testimony, he was asked why he asked for the officer's badge number. He said because of certain things he had heard. He was asked why he didn't say something to Mr. R.? On the basis of his experience in working with a group, he knew he shouldn't talk to a defendant in the matter, but to the officer. I would expect the officer to act in a more mature fashion than the defendant . . . I don't think there is any proof that the defendant violated this statute.

Some of you may have come to the conclusion that T. was morally guilty, that it was not an error of his heart, but his intellect. You are not being asked to find him morally guilty, but legally guilty of resisting arrest . . .

This case has much to do with the way T. said, "This is the way riots start." There was nothing wrong with that when he saw R. being choked. A reasonable amount of force could have been used to make this arrest. At least say, "You are under arrest, put up your hands" . . . and this was not said. T.'s saying, "This is the way riots start," was reasonable. I hope you will render a decision we could be proud of as Americans . . . There is a poem of Walt Whitman's . . . "If there is a reasonable doubt, do justice and you too will look at the sign of the stars as truth and justice."

Part V: Judge H.'s Concluding Instructions to the Jury

. . . weigh the evidence and apply the law and reach a just verdict. This verdict on each of the charges must express the opinion of each of you. The attorneys for the defense are entitled to the opinion of each of you. When you reach a judgment, you must not change it merely to bring about a unanimous verdict. Render your verdict according to your final decision. Do not speculate to be true any insinuations — questions are not evidence. Defendant in a criminal action is considered innocent until proven guilty beyond a reasonable doubt . . . evidence of . . . character involved is regarded by the law as evidence . . . evidence of the character of the witness should be considered for the purpose of determining credibility . . . every witness is presumed to speak the truth . . . a witness wilfully false in one . . . is to be distrusted in all . . . you may treat all of their evidence on suspicion . . . however, discrepancies do not mean a witness should be discredited. Each witness may see the same thing differently . . . the rise or fall of my voice should not be considered to influence . . . you. Go now, and bring back a just decision.

Part VI: Budd Schulberg's Epilogue

The jury was out all afternoon and into the evening before rendering their verdict. On three counts: two against defendant R.; one against T. As we sat there waiting we could hear loud discussion crackling into anger. We felt like an audience that somehow had passed through the proscenium arch of "Twelve Angry Men." At last they returned. They stood 12 to 0 for the acquittal of T.

It was a long, long trail from that opening morning when the first, bored public defender had shown us the police charges against T with "Don't you see here what this boy has done?" Between that conviction without trial and our Negro Public Defender's appeal to Walt Whitman and American justice to which both Judge and the jury responded, there spread the whole spectrum from the frequent miscarriage of justice for the black man in America to the occasional and hopeful twelve-strike for justice.

This trial went unnoticed in the local papers of Los Angeles. To the local press it may have seemed just another traffic case, involving an unknown and insignificant teen-ager, one of thousands of invisible men in the dark ghetto. Actually the incident leading to young T.'s arrest was almost identical with the one involving the Frye brothers and their mother which sparked the furious fires of '65. That was the true significance of the T. case. In the eyes of T., the police in their rough handling of a traffic violator, were inviting another riot. In the eyes of the police it was T. who was guilty of setting the fuse. Although unreported it was a trial of profound significance for Los Angeles, both as to content and verdict. It was, in its small way, a microcosm of the tensions that pulse on in Los Angeles. When it came to the attention of a columnist for the *New York Post,* Pete Hamill, he devoted his entire space to it. He saw it for what it was, an obscure, yet monumental trial. It may not be literature but we thought it deserved to be included in this book because it is the stuff of literature. For out of the T.'s and their trials both literal and figurative are stories waiting to be told.

Editor's Postscript

Every anthology inevitably involves both heartbreak and injustice. Somewhat to atone for both, the editors wish to mention those writers whose works were seriously considered but, for one reason or another, could not be included in the final table of contents.

Poems and essays by Ellen Brown were narrow misses. Unfortunately, a new poem, "Like It Is, Parts I and II," and other sharper short pieces were submitted too late for inclusion. Rozelle Leavell's novel-in-progress, *Forestville,* is extremely promising, but it was felt an excerpt would not do justice to the whole. There were also editorials by Norris Dabbs, comic sketches by Helen Autry, and an essay on Watts by Jayne Howard.

Poetry by Lloyd Honoré, John H. Jones, and Margaret Terrell and contributions from Mildred Walters, Charles Cyrus Thomas, and Adelia Davis also reached us too late for consideration.

A question of timing prevented our including impressive work from writers who joined the Workshop after the Table of Contents had been selected. Otherwise we would surely have included the short stories "Just Close Your Eyes" by Martha Tucker, "Daddy Was A Numbers Runner" by Louise Meriwether, a sheaf of prose poems by Quincy Troupe, and a moving play by Edward Baldwin.

To those we have mentioned, and to other aspiring writers who joined the Workshop too late for their work to be appraised, our apologies and regrets. Hopefully *From the Ashes* will be followed by a companion volume, *Black Phoenix,* in which the contributions mentioned above and the work of other writers now active in the Watts Writers' Workshop at Douglass House will yet have their day in print.

— *Budd Schulberg*

About the Editor

Budd Schulberg considers Hollywood his hometown although he was born in New York City. The son of B. P. Schulberg, a motion picture pioneer who was for many years in charge of Paramount, Budd Schulberg became fascinated with the theme of "the failure of success" and found Hollywood an ideal laboratory for the study of this star-spangled phenomenon. He was educated at Los Angeles High School, Deerfield Academy, and Dartmouth College, where he edited the daily paper, majored with Honors in Sociology, and won an intercollegiate story contest. Immediately after graduation he began publishing short stories in Story, The New Yorker, *and other literary journals. From 1937 to 1940 he served a term as an apprentice screenwriter for producers Sam Goldwyn, David O. Selznick, and Walter Wanger, for whom he collaborated with F. Scott Fitzgerald. During that same period, he wrote a series of Hollywood stories for* Esquire, The Saturday Evening Post, *and other popular magazines. His first novel,* What Makes Sammy Run?, *published in 1941, was voted by critics the best first-novel of that year; the success he had tried to study objectively came to him when he was still in his middle twenties. Although he prefers the novel to all other written forms, Mr. Schulberg has established a reputation as one of Hollywood's most celebrated screenwriters.* On the Waterfront *won him an "Oscar" as well as awards from foreign film festivals and the Screen Writers Guild.* A Face in the Crowd *won him further honors in that field. Since* What Makes Sammy Run? *he has published three other novels —* The Harder They Fall, The Disenchanted, *and* Waterfront *—and a collection of short stories,* Some Faces in the Crowd. *He has also had two successes on the Broadway stage. He lives most of the year in Beverly Hills, where his actress wife Geraldine Brooks, a critics' favorite, is occupied with her film and television work. The Schulbergs also maintain a residence in Mexico City, where Budd goes on occasional "digs" in pursuit of his lifelong interest in archeology. Aside from his literary activities, and his efforts in behalf of marble workers in Vermont, longshoremen in New York, and the people of Watts (where he has founded an unprecedented literary center), Mr. Schulberg is also a national authority on boxing, writing extensively on the subject and, for a time, co-managing a heavyweight of international reputation. He is currently at work on a new novel.*

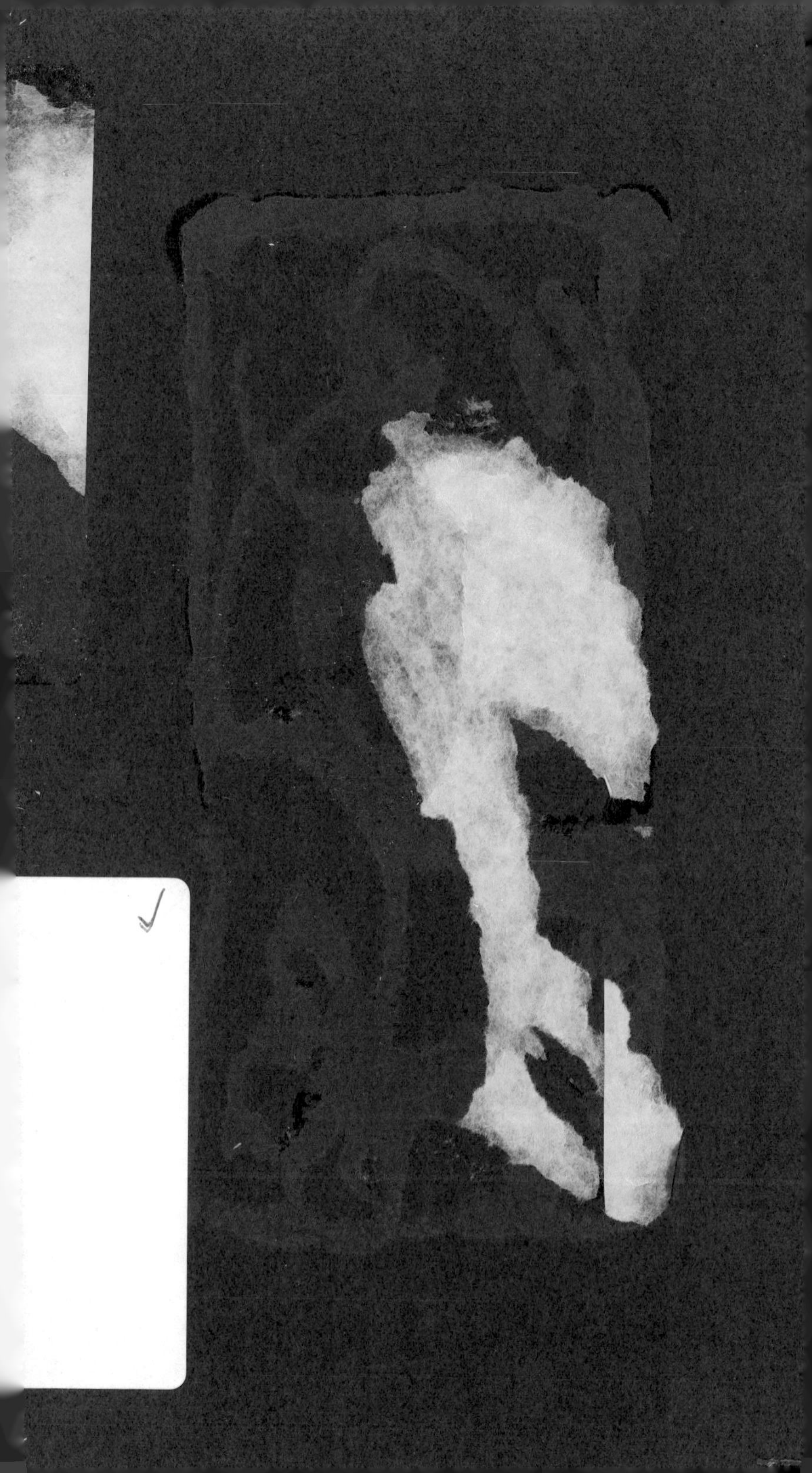